LAN(
DL

A selection of words and anecdotes
from around Lancashire

by
Camilla Zajac

BRADWELL
BOOKS

1

Published by Bradwell Books
9 Orgreave Close Sheffield S13 9NP
Email: books@bradwellbooks.co.uk

British Library Cataloguing in Publication Data:
a catalogue record for this book is available from
the British Library.

1st Edition

ISBN: 9781902674964

Print: Gomer Press, Llandysul, Ceredigion SA44 4JL

Artwork and design by: Andrew Caffrey

Photograph Credits:
Unless stated otherwise, all images are reproduced with
the kind permission of Lancashire Archives.

E

Ealin – a shed set against another building; a lean-to

Eddercrop – a spider

Eend-way – outright; at once; to the end

Elders – ancestors, parents, betters, elders

Eldin' – fuel or fire

Ettle – stingy

F

Fadder – father

Fadge – a burden, part of a horse's load

Faffment – nonsense

Fairish-on – elderly

Farrant – becoming, decent, nice
(applied to action or dress)

Fettle – to mend, improve, set right, dress

Fewtrils – little things

Flutterment – excitement

Foisty – having a musty or bad smell or taste

Foo-scutter – silly boasting talk

Fratch – quarrelsome; to quarrel, to dispute

Fremd – a stranger or guest

G

Gad-about – an idle, rambling person

Gadwaud – a long stick

Gaffer – a master

Gammerstang – an awkward, tall, slender person, male or female

Garden-twod – a large toad

Gawmin' – understanding, considering, cogitating

Gawsterin' – boasting

Ginn – a road or passage down to the sea

Ginnel – a narrow entry; a covered passage between houses

Glizzen – lightning

Gloppen – to astonish, to surprise

Gobbin – an ignorant, clownish person

Gollop – to swallow hastily or greedily

Grumble-belly – a discontented person

Gullook – go and look; see for yourself

Gumption – ability combined with good sense

H

Hack – a pickaxe, a stone-pick or mattock, used by excavators

Hackslaver – an objectionable blockhead; a silly fellow

Haffle – to hesitate, to prevaricate

Hammil – a hamlet

Hanch-apple – an old name for a version of apple bobbing which is usually played at Halloween

Hansel – a gift given to the first purchaser; also to have the first use of anything

Happen – probably, perhaps, possibly

Hattock – a corn sheaf

Haybant – a twisted band of hay

Hay-moo – a stack of hay; moo is the pronunciation of mow which means the pile or stack of hay which has been mowed; a mow is also the loft or chamber in which hay or corn is laid up

Heawse-place – the living room in a cottage

Henky-penky – trickery

I

Irnin – cheese-making

Ivin– ivy

J

Jackstones – a child's game, played with a large marble and the knuckle-bones of a sheep; also with small white pebbles or jackstones; the same game was also known as bobber and kibs

Jannock – a dark-coloured bread or cake made of oatmeal, or of coarse wheatmeal; this word was also metaphorically applied to anything or any action that is honest or thorough

Jerry – bad, defective, and deceptive, hence the phrase *'jerry-built'*

Jerry-shop – public house

Jiddy – to agree

Jinny-green-teeth – literally the green scum on ponds, but supposed to imply the presence of a water sprite or 'boggart'; a terror to children as they pass the pond on which the appearance is seen

Jobbernowl – a dunce or dolt

Johnny-raw – a foolish or stupid person

Just-now – in a short time, after a little interval

K

Kale – broth or pottage

Kales – the game of ninepins

Kame – a comb

Keepin' company – courting, being betrothed

Keevilly – unsteady

Kenspak – easy to know

Kenspeckle – distinctive feature of a person, either individually or from their clothing

Kin-cough – the whooping cough

Kinkin' – laughing

All change: tram line workers in Fishergate, Preston remove
old horse-drawn tram lines in readiness for laying electric tram lines.
The service started in 1904.

L

Lake – to play

Lankister-lowp – leap-frog

Lant – to disappoint

Lant – stale urine, generally referred to as 'owd lant'; this was frequently used by Lancashire cottagers for scouring or cleaning blankets and other woollen cloths and for various medicinal purposes: every yard or garden would have had a container for storing the home's supply of lant

Latter-end – the time of death

Leetsome – light, cheerful, pleasant-looking

Let-on – to tell a secret

M

Maddle – to confuse or to irritate

Madlin – a flighty, extravagant person

Mangy – ill-tempered, peevish

Manigate – a straight road over bog or moss land

Market-fresh – drunk

Marlock – a playful trick, a prank, a game, a joke, fun

Mawkin – a scarecrow

Meeterly – tolerably well, comfortably

Minder – the name given to one of the workers in a spinning mill

Mits – a woollen covering for the hands which leave the fingers and half the thumb bare; also strong leather gloves without partitions for the fingers, used when handling thorns and prickly shrubs, or repairing fences

Moonleet-flittin' – the stealthy removal of household furniture in the night to avoid payment of rent

Mooter – mill-toll; a quantity of meal or flour taken by the miller as his due for grinding

N

Nappy – merry, joyous, under the influence of alcohol

Neck-or-nowt – entirely, altogether

Neet-crow – a night-bird, a way of referring to a person fond of staying up late

Nesh – tender, weak, delicate, soft

Never-heed – don't notice, take no care

Noonin – the rest from labour at noon

Noonscawpe – rest taken at noon

Nope – a small blow

Notchels – leftover food fragments

O

Oandurth – afternoon

Oddment – scraps, fragments, trifles, remnants, pieces of furniture

Ogreath – right, straight, perfect

Oon – oven

Othergates – otherwise

Othersome – others

Out-comlin – a stranger

P

Pace-egg – a hard-boiled egg, dyed or stained, and presented as an Easter offering

Pace-eggers – mummers, who went around in groups at Easter, usually performing the old masque of George and the Dragon

Paddock – toad or frog

Paddock-stool – a fungus, a toadstool

Panbindin' – a payment or compensation for an injury

Pickle – a condition of difficulty or disgrace, confusion

Playin'-part – being out of work

Pobbies – a child's dish of bread and warm milk

Pod – to sulk

Podgy – stout and of short stature

Q

Querk – to cheat, to overreach

Quern – a hand-mill for grinding corn

Quick-sticks – a short space of time

Quocker – one who goes harvesting to a distance far from their local area

Miles of smiles: children outside Chorley Cinema. Davy Crockett and the River Pirates was released 1956 while The African Lion came out in 1955.

R

Racketty – careless, thoughtless

Racklesome – reckless

Raggot – a rough, disorderly person

Raggotin – rambling about; living in a disorderly way

Raggy – broken and stormy

Raither-of-oather – almost; equivalent to the phrase 'on the whole'

Ram-bazz – suddenly and with great force

Rapscallion – a wild and reckless person

Ratey – rough (applied to the weather)

Ratton – a rat

Raw-head – a term of horror used to frighten children

Rawky – damp, foggy

Read – to perceive, to make out, to understand

Rear an' ferrin – the ridge and furrow in a field

Reawk – to get together; to associate

Reawly – sleepy, unwashed

S

Sand-knocker – a sand-grinder; this occupation was formerly common in Lancashire, sand being more frequently used, not only for the purpose of cleaning, but as a kind of ornament, and to preserve cleanliness;

after a floor had been washed, 'sanding' it was an almost universal custom

Sapless – foolish, witless

Scrowe – a disturbance, an uproar; a bewildering state of affairs

Seely – silly, foolish, simple

Seemin'-glass – a looking-glass, a mirror

Settle – a long wooden couch, with arms and wooden back

Shaffle-horn – one who shirks work; a shiftless person

Shive – a slice, generally a slice of bread

Skelboose – a passage by the side of a cattle stall, made so that a man can get to the fodder-rack in front of the cattle

Sowe – the mixture of flour and water used by the handloom weaver for sizing the warp

Sprote – to brag, to amplify, to exaggerate, to display

Sproze – to talk big, to swagger

T

Tackler – a name given to an overlooker in a weaving mill

Tastril – a small keg or barrel

Tatchin'-end – a thread with a bristle attached to it; used in shoemaking

Tent – to watch, to mind

Tenter – a watcher; the person in charge of certain machines in a mill

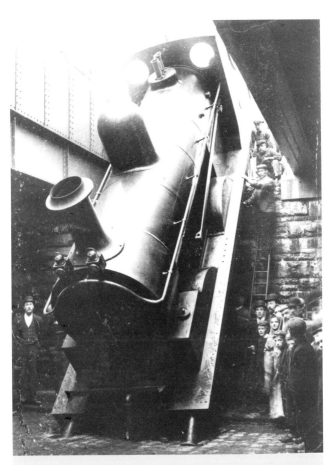

Crowds at the scene of a train accident in Lonsdale Street, Accrington in September 1899 after it crashed through the buffers and came down in the street between two sections of the railway bridge

Tharcake – a cake made from meal, treacle and butter, and eaten on the night of the fifth of November

Thick-an'-thin – difficulties, obstacles

Think-on – to remember

Threep – to argue, to contend for a special point, to dispute

Throdkin – a cake made of oatmeal and bacon

Toothsome – dainty, palatable

U

Umbrell – an umbrella

Unbethink – to remember, to reflect

Uncuth – strange

Underbree – a bright light appearing under clouds

Underneigh – underneath

Ungain – awkward, inconvenient

Un-sneck – to unlatch or unfasten a door

Uppish – proud, conceited

V

Varra – very

Viewsome – handsome, striking to the eye

W

Waft – a draught

Wakin'-time – the time or period of the wakes

Walk-mill – a fulling mill, walker, a fuller; in the early Manchester directories all the fullers and cloth-dressers were called walkers

Wang-tooth – a molar tooth

Wheem – handy, convenient

Wheem – innocent-looking, quiet

Whewt – to whistle

Wutherin' – rushing, overpowering

Y

Yammer – to long for, to yearn after

Yarber – a gatherer of herbs

Yary – acrid, strong-flavoured

Yate – a gate, a fence

Yearnstfully – earnestly

Yerr – to hear

Yonderly – anxious, absent-minded, vacant

Yo-neet – a merry night

Yorney – a fool

The Red Rose of Lancashire
Shutterstock ©Nicolas Raymond

What's in a name?

Lancashire takes its title from the city of Lancaster whose name means 'Roman fort on the River Lune'. Lancashire became a county only in 1182, making it one of the youngest historic counties of England! Known as the Red Rose County because the first Earl of Lancaster used the rose as a heraldic symbol, the county took on its floral symbol for good in 1485, after the Battle of Bosworth Field.

Why do people in Lancashire make a loyal toast to 'the Queen, Duke of Lancaster'?

People at formal occasions and Lancastrian regiments of the armed forces make a toast to *'the Queen, Duke of Lancaster'* because of Lancashire's heritage as a county palatine. A county palatine was a county in which the local nobleman (here it was the Duke of Lancaster) had powers which matched those enjoyed by the reigning monarch over the country as a whole. Lancashire was made a county – or duchy – palatine in 1351. It kept a lot of its judicial privileges right up till 1873. In 1399, the Dukedom of Lancaster was then merged into the Crown. But even now, it is separate from other royal lands and is managed by the Duchy of Lancaster. The title of Chancellor of the Duchy of Lancaster is still used by a member of the cabinet. That's why you'll hear people making a toast to *'The Queen, Duke of Lancaster'* to this day.

Another pate hke his;
It's o' crom-full o' ancientry,
An' Roman haw-pennies!

Excerpt from–'Come, Mary, Link thi Arm i' Mine'

From *Lancashire Songs* by EDWIN WAUGH, published 1866

Come, Mary, link thi arm i' mine,
An' lilt away wi' me;
An' dry that little drop o' brine
Fro' th' corner o' thi e'e;
Th' momin' dew i'th' heather-bell's
A bonny gem o' weet;
That tear a different story tells, —
It pains my heart to see't.
So, Mary, link thi arm i' mine.

No lordly ho' o'th' country-side's
So welcome to my view,
As th' little cottage where abides
My sweetheart, kind an' true;
But, there's a nook beside yon spring,
An' iv thae'll share't wi' me;
Aw'll buy tho th' prattist gowden ring
That ever theaw did see!
So, Mary, link thi arm i' mine.

My feyther's gan mo forty peawnd,
I' silver an' i' gowd;
An' a bonny bit o' garden greawnd,
O'th' mornin' side o'th' fowd;
An' a honsome bible, clen an' new.
To read for days to come; —
There's leaves for writin' names in, too,
Like th' owd un at's awhoam.
So, Mary, link thi arm i' mine.

Excerpt from–'The Royal Visit to Wigan (June 1873)'

From *Poems, Songs & Recitations in the Lancashire Dialect* by
JAMES BROWN OF HAIGH, published 1881

Havin' a bit o' leighshure toime,
Aw'll just sit deawn an' pen a rhoime,
Abeawt that greight hospishus day
Whiich Wiggin shortly will display.

On til' third o' June aw understand,
Th' owd burro' will bi deckd' quoite grand.
An nowt bud reet, for on that day,
A RKoyal pair will visit Haigh.

Wheer eawr respected Earl, aw know,
Will on their Highnesses bestow,

Thoose good things money con procure.
To mak' their happiness secure.

To' should see th' vast preparashuns,
Up ud th' Ho an' throo th' plantashuns;
Besides the noble House o' Haigh,
Will feast some hundreds on thad day.

Leds cheer booath Lord an' Lady C,
For helpin' on th' Infirmary;
Their koindly akshuns, awve no deowt,
Hav' browt this grand event abeawt.

Becose, wi me yo'll o agree,
Thad they invoited Royalty,
Afther th' Wiggin Corporashun
Had sent up their depitashun.
Awm shure eawr wealthy worthy Mayor
Every good thing will prepare,
Eor th' Royal guests, an' th' rest o'th' bunch,
Thad he intends axin to lunch.

His spred nil boath bi rich an' grand,
Becose he's money at command;
Aw'll bet a shillin' to a groat
He's cash enough to sink a boat.

Awm gradely glad thad Mesther Simm
Eawr able chief, ull dine wi him;
His wurship's very koind indeed,
For thus invitin' him to feed.

The Pemberton Library Episode

From *Poems, Songs & Recitations in the Lancashire Dialect* by JAMES BROWN OF HAIGH, published 1881

Aw took up yoar papper last wick,
A few little bits to glance o'er,
An' wurn't aw surproised for to see
That meetin' which cawst sich uproar.

An as aw've bin axt bi sum friends
To put a few verses i' rhoime
Abeawt the disgraceful affair
Aw'll do so, though stinted for toime.

Directly the schoo' clock struck seven,
H. Widdows geet up to propose
That owd fermer Whoite shud tak th' cheer
Until the proceedins did close.
Wich sum mon soon jumpt up to secund,
His name they coed Tetton, aw think.
An' judgin' fro' th' chap's windy talk,

34

Aw guess he'd had summat to drink.

Beawt puttin the moshun to th' meetin'
Owd Whoite at once popt into th' chair,
Afore Mester Barrett arroived,
Wich yo mun admit were unfair.

The Local Board foak wur axt fust
A ratepayer's meetin' t' convene,
Then why not let th' reet un presoide?
For shame on yo actin so mean.

Children gather in Fox Lane in Leyland. In the past, this part of
Fox Lane was called Union Street. Cotton weaving was undertaken in the
cellars because the cotton was easier to work in cool, damp conditions.

Whoite owt to ha' shift o' one soide,
An gan Mester Barrett his place;
Things wud ha' gone far better on,
Besoides lessenin' th' shame an disgrace.

Partington seem'd quite astonish'd
An' hardly cud tell whot to do;
Whoile Barrett an' o his supporters
Appeart likewoise in a stew.
Charnock, fro' Wiggin, spoke eawt plain,
An' towd 'em regardless o' feor,
His candid opinion wur,
That Barrett shud ockipy th' cheor.

Heawever, it o' wur no use,
They couldn't get owd Whoite to stur;
Theerfore, they had no other plan
But to tak matters just as they wur.

Aw'm towd sum o' th' roughs wur quite fresh,
Not wi drink in' hot coffee an' tay,
But sum nowty stuff wich it seems,
Droives senses an' rayson away.

Memories of Lancashire Life

Excerpt from *Lancashire Memories* (1879)
By LOUISA POTTER, Published 1879

Our country neighbours

I was seven years old (and now I am — no matter what) when, owing to my mother's illness, it was thought desirable to send me out of the way for a time; so I was packed off to my grandpapa in the country, greatly to my own satisfaction — perhaps rather more so than to his. It was a populous manufacturing district, still the country, inasmuch as it was some miles from a town. The poorer classes, almost without exception, were hand-loom weavers, earning seven shillings a week by sixteen hours of toil a day.

If the family was numerous, the mothers and younger children were employed in winding bobbins to supply the father's or elder brothers and sisters looms, and so eked out a subsistence without leaving the family roof. I liked nothing better than sitting with the weaver on the bench, watching the work with its mysteries and difficulties; the shuttle flying to and fro with such precision, the two long brushes, dipped in "sow," or sour paste, smoothing the warp under and over, followed by that awful red-hot salamander that dried it without burning; but the wonder of all was, how the feet could hit the six or eight treddles below accurately without looking. I thought I could have managed old Sammy Ogden's loom, that had only two treddles, for he wove nothing but coarse grey calico. The young women sung at their work, loud and shrill, *"Sally in our Alley,"* and a favourite ballad about going to the races, of which all I recollect was that the company came " from Chorley and Chow- bent, likewise from Cockey Moor. The continued monotonous "clickety-click" of the loom was heard from every cottage door, and to this day the old familiar sound conjures up a host of memories that would otherwise be dormant for ever. I often begged Lizzy Fallows to let me wind the bobbins for her, whilst she went off to a game at "hop-flag," but the weavers never liked my winding. When the thread breaks, the ends are fastened together with what is called a weavers knot, but I found this troublesome ; so when a thread broke, I wetted the end, stuck it on, and wound again, which made a fault in the cloth.

"Tim Bobbin" - 'The Father of the Lancashire Dialect'

Tim Bobbin was the pseudonym of John Collier who is known as 'the father of the Lancashire Dialect'. He earned this grand title thanks to the fact that he wrote extensively in his local dialect. Probably his best known work is A View of the Lancashire Dialect; containing the Adventures and Misfortunes of a Lancashire Clown by Tim Bobbin. Published in 1750, the book is a comic dialogue between two characters, Thomas and Mary. It also provides a detailed glossary of Lancashire words and phrases collected over many years.

But it was a book published in 1850 which brought Collier even more fame and fortune. This was the somewhat wordily titled Tim Bobbin's Tummus and Meary ; with His Rhymes and an Enlarged and Amended Glossary of Words and Phrases, Chiefly Used by the Rural Population of the Manufacturing Districts of South Lancashire. It was the first attempt at creating a scientific survey of the Lancashire dialect, earning Collier the name of 'the Father of Lancashire Dialect'. It went on to significantly influence many other Lancashire writers. An eccentric character, when he wasn't writing, playing music or working in his day job as the master of a village school, Collier was fond - and famed for - creating wicked caricatures, for which he was given the name 'the Lancashire Hogarth'.

John Collier

Excerpt from Memoir of John Collier

From Tim Bobbin's Tummus and Meary; with His Rhymes and an Enlarged and Amended Glossary of Words and Phrases, Chiefly Used by the Rural Population of the Manufacturing Districts of South Lancashire.

"Several writers have endeavoured, both in prose and rhyme, to express themselves in the Lancashire dialect, but, with one or two exceptions, they have not succeeded. The fact is, that until the present edition, there has not been any true glossary to write the dialect by, that of Tim Bobbin, if truth may be stated, being itself far from correct. I may be blamed by some, for being thus candid, but the fact had often been forced on my attention, both from my own observation and that of others...His Lancashire Dialect was not the spoken dialect of any one district of the county; and his friend Mr. Townley, of Belfield, in writing to a gentleman at Manchester, describes him as taking note of every quaint, odd, out of the way term, or phrase, which he heard during his peram-bulations in different parts of the country, and incorporating them in his *View of the Lancashire Dialect*.

Writing in dialect

With a language as vivid as 'Lanky Talk', it's no surprise that Lancashire produced a whole crop of dialect writers besides 'Tim Bobbin', particularly in the 19th century. These authors brought their local dialect to life through songs and poems. Some of these figures are celebrated at the Lancashire Dialect Writers' Memorial in Bradfield Park in Rochdale.

The writers that helped to capture Lancashire's dialect included:

William Harrison Ainsworth

"She would rather be an old man's darling than a young man's warling."

WILLIAM HARRISON AINSWORTH

Born in 1805 in Manchester, Ainsworth became a popular romantic novelist. He published his first two novels, Sir John Chiverton and Rockwood in 1834. He then went on to produce no less than 40 historical romances! Many of his books feature local dialects. Some of his most well known works are Old St. Paul's, Windsor Castle and The Lancashire Witches.

Samuel Bamford

Samuel Bamford was an important figure in the history of the area. Born in 1788 in the village of Middleton, he went on to become a high profile radical and writer. After first starting out as a weaver and a warehouseman, Bamford became involved in political activities and became a poet and a journalist. His political views inspired and shaped his writings. He wrote both in standard English as well as in the Lancashire dialect. His works include Passages in the Life of a Radical (for which he is best known today), Walks Among the Workers of the cotton districts and Walks in

South Lancashire. As Bamford grew in political awareness, he became increasingly interested in dialect literature and was sometimes seen at the meetings of the Sun Inn circle of Lancashire poets and authors in Manchester. This interest evolved into a glossary of the Lancashire dialect, produced with William Gaskell and the Manchester Literary and Philosophical Society. First published in 1850, this glossary became the basis for future Lancashire dialect dictionaries.

Margaret Lahee

"When we lay deaun life's shuttle an' stone before the greyt judge,
He'll wont to know what sooat of a piece we'n woven,
An how many floats there's in it,
He winnot care abeawt eawr hee seaundin' names an' worldly possessions.
He'll ax us how we got em an what we did wi' em."

MARGARET REBECCA LAHEE, as quoted on the Lancashire Dialect Writers' Memorial in Bradfield Park, Rochdale.

Born in Carlow, Ireland in 1831, Margaret Lahee spent a great deal of her life in Rochdale. She became involved in capturing the local dialect through writing and went on to became one of only a very small number of female dialect writers of the 1800s to have her work published.

Edwin Waugh

"If a man was a pair of steam-looms, how carefully would he be oiled, and tended, and mended, and made to do all that a pair of looms could do. What a loom, full of miraculous faculties, is he compared to these—the master-piece of nature for creative power and for wonderful variety of excellent capabilities! Yet, with what a profuse neglect he is cast away, like the cheapest rubbish on the earth!"

EDWIN WAUGH

Known as the "Prince of dialect poets" and a true champion of the Lancashire dialect, Edwin Waugh was born in Rochdale in 1817. In 1855, he published his first book, Sketches of Lancashire Life and Localities. But it was in 1856 that he published his dialect poem, Come whoam to thi childer an' me. Like Lahee, Waugh is now commemorated on the Lancashire Dialect Writers' Memorial in Rochdale.

Lanky Talk: Today's Lancashire phrases

Known affectionately as *'Lanky Talk'*, today's Lancashire dialect is still packed with great turns of phrase! Here are some examples, spelled phonetically to help with pronunciation!

'Weerst bin?' – Where have you been?

'Weerst gooin?' – Where are you going?

'Ast bin?' – Have you been?

'Am gooin wom' – I am going home

'Owd on' – Hold on

'Nay tha cawnt' – No you cannot

'Gerr away wi thi' – I don't believe you

'Ah cud eyt a buttered frog/a scabby dog' – I'm hungry

'Mi belly thinks mi throat's bin cut' – I'm very hungry!

'Ee's fair bowlegged wi brass' – He's very rich

'Put th'wood in'th'ole' – Close the door

'Tha meks a betta doower than a winda' – You're blocking my view

'Standin theer leyke cheese at fourpence' – Hanging around

'Once every Preston Guild' – Not very often

(the Preston Guild takes place every 20 years. Look out for more about it further on in this book)

'Tha's bin aytin vinnigger offa knife' – A response to a sharp remark

'Wudta be as sharp in mi grave?' – A sarcastic remark made to a person who takes over someone else's seat very quickly

'More faces than a church clock' – A fickle person

'I may be cabbage looking, but I'm not green' – I'm not completely naive!

'Ger off mi fuut!' – An expression of disbelief

'You're as awkard as Dick's hatband' – You're making things very complicated

'Slur thy clogs' – Don't act too hastily

'Eh, ah can see Moogy Dawson's bin wi' ee' – You're looking scruffy

'Eeh, ah woudn't part wi it fer a golden vayse' – I wouldn't part with it for anything

'Well I'll go to the bottom of our stairs' – An expression of surprise

'He hasn't all his chairs at home' – He isn't very bright

Wish you were here?
This 1920s postcard uses satire to highlight the reality of workers'
lives in Lancashire. The caption reads: *'It's nice to have a home
of your own and sit by your own fireside.'*

towards the relief of their starving neighbours, sometimes even when they themselves ought to be receiving relief, if their true condition was known.

I heard of several shopkeepers who had not taken more across their counters for weeks past than would pay their rents, and some were not doing even so much as that. This is one painful bit of the kernel of life in Blackburn just now, which is concealed by the quiet shell of outward appearance. Beyond this unusual quietness, a stranger will not see much of the pinch of the times, unless he goes deeper; for the people of Lancashire never were remarkable for hawking their troubles much about the world. In the present untoward pass, their deportment, as a whole, has been worthy of themselves, and their wants have been worthily met by their own neighbours.

I hear on all hands that there is hardly any town in Lancashire suffering so much as Preston. The reason why the stroke has fallen so heavily here, lies in the nature of the trade. In the first place, Preston is almost purely a cotton town. There are two or three flax mills, and two or three ironworks, of no great extent; but, upon the whole, there is hardly any variety of employment there to lighten the disaster which has befallen its one absorbing occupation. There is comparatively little weaving in Preston; it is a town mostly engaged in spinning. The cotton used there is nearly all what is called 'Middling American', the very kind which is now most scarce and dear. The yarns of Preston are known by the name of 'Blackburn

Counts'. They range from 28's up to 60's, and they enter largely into the manufacture of goods for the India market.

These things partly explain why Preston is more deeply overshadowed by the particular gloom of the times than many other places in Lancashire. About half-past nine on Tuesday morning last, I set out with an old acquaintance to call upon a certain member of the Relief Committee, in George's Ward. He is the manager of a cotton mill in that quarter, and he is well known and much respected among the working people. When we entered the mill-yard, all was quiet there, and the factory was still and silent. But through the office window we could see the man we wanted. He was accompanied by one of the proprietors of the mill, turning over the relief books of the ward. I soon found that he had a strong sense of humour, as well as a heart welling over with tenderness. He pointed to some of the cases in his books. The first was that of an old man, an overlooker of a cotton mill. His family was thirteen in number; three of the children were under ten years of age; seven of the rest were factory operatives; but the whole family had been out of work for several months. When in full employment the joint earnings of the family amounted to 80s. a week; but, after struggling on in the hope of better times, and exhausting the savings of past labour, they had been brought down to the receipt of charity at last, and for sixteen weeks gone by the whole thirteen had been living upon 6s. a week from the relief fund. They had no other resource. I went to see them at their own house afterwards, and it certainly was a pattern of cleanliness, with the little household gods there still. Seeing that house, a stranger would never dream that the family was living on an average income of less than sixpence a head per week.

Who were the Cotton Queens?

Lancashire's cotton industry did make a comeback, but only in a limited way. The Cotton Queen competition was started in 1930 to encourage public interest in the cotton industry. It was an annual three-week event hosted in Blackpool. The chosen Cotton Queen would spend her year's reign promoting cotton at different events across the country.

In celebration of cotton: the Cotton Queens, including Burnley's, in 1937 at the Empress Ballroom, Burnley

Sadly, despite the best efforts of the industry and help from the government, British companies could simply not produce cotton cloth as cheaply as their overseas competitors.

Mining

The drive towards industrialisation also created a greater need for coal and of course mining. This drive came not only from the growing textiles industry in the county, but from iron and chemical works, the engineering industry and others. It led to a growing use of barges to transport coal. Lancashire was home to what was known as one of the most important coalfields – the Lancashire Coalfield.

The coalfield was right at the cutting edge of advances in coal mining and led to the development of Lancashire's first canals, using steam engines and supporting industrialisation. The pits on the coalfield were at their most productive in 1907 when more than 26 million tons of coal were produced. During the first quarter of the 20th century, an average of nearly 20 million tons of coal was produced annually by a workforce of 100,000 men! By 1967, just 21 collieries remained, compared with 358 back in 1907.

Workers at Moorfield Colliery in Altham

What happened in Wakes Week?

If you mentioned Wakes Week back in the 'cotton belt' in Lancashire's industrial age, you would have seen many happy faces. This is because Wakes Week was the annual summer break – a week off work. The tradition meant that local towns took their weeks off at different times to one another. From June right through to September, one town was on holiday each week. Entire towns would close down while their populations headed off on holiday. This break was unpaid at first, but most workers made a contribution to a holiday savings club.

Finally in 1907, workers reached an agreement with their employers for 12 days' annual holiday. However, paid holidays didn't come about until the 1940s and 1950s. The Wakes Week tradition started to disappear in the 1960s.

We're off for Wakes Week! Crowds gather at Padiham Railway
Station for a Blackpool or Southport excursion special

Land of industrial invention

The rise and rise of Lancashire through industrialisation led to some very important inventions. These include:

The Flying Shuttle

Bury man John Kay invented a mohair twisting and carding engine as well as improving metal loom reeds. His invention of the Flying Shuttle more than doubled the speed of handloom weaving! Previously, two workers had had to be employed for weaving broadcloth. With a loom equipped with a flying shuttle, broadcloth could be produced by just one weaver.

The Spinning Jenny

Thanks to the 'Spinning Jenny', a number of wool or cotton threads could be produced by one person, simultaneously spinning yarn onto eight or more spindles. James Hargreaves, a Blackburn-born handloom weaver, started out by looking for a way to increase the output of spun yarn. Before this invention, it had taken six spinners to keep one handloom weaver supplied with enough yarn!

The Water Frame

Created by Preston man, Richard Arkwright, the Water or Spinning Frame was the very first powered and automatic textile machine. It produced stronger threads for yarns. The spinning frame was also important because it was the first machine that could spin cotton threads.

The Spinning Mule

This machine is seen as having revolutionised the Lancashire Cotton industry. Samuel Crompton built his machine to combine the best aspects of Hargreaves' Spinning Jenny and Arkwright's Water Frame. The mule spun a fine yarn to a quality high enough to allow it to produce fine cloths like muslin. The mass production of these fabrics opened up new markets. It also drove the movement of the spinning process from home to factory.

The Lancashire Loom

The Lancashire Loom was a semi-automatic power loom invented by James Bullough and William Kenworthy in 1842. It proved to be an essential part of the Lancashire cotton industry for more than a hundred years. A more advanced version of this power loom went on to become known as the Lancashire Loom and became an essential part of the weaving process for many years.

Not forgetting Thomas Highs (1718–1803)

No exploration of Lancashire inventions is complete without mentioning Thomas Highs. While he died

Unusual Lancashire Customs

World Black Pudding Throwing Championship

Like black pudding? Then you'll love the rather strange Lancashire custom, the Black Pudding Throwing Championship, which takes place every year in Ramsbottom. Contestants throw three black puddings each at a pile of 21 Yorkshire puddings set on a six-metre plinth. You're the winner if you manage to knock down the highest number of Yorkshire puddings in three goes!

Egg rolling at Holcombe Hill, Ramsbottom

Ramsbottom is the site of yet another intriguing Lancashire tradition. Each year on Good Friday people get together at the foot of the town's Holcombe Hill. Both adults and children happily take part in an egg rolling 'eggstravanza' with boiled eggs.

The Britannia Coconut Dancers of Bacup

Based in Bacup, the Britannia Coconut Dancers are folk dancers with a particularly unusual appearance. They have blackened faces and wear brightly coloured clothes. Every Easter Saturday, they gather at the Travellers Rest Public House with the Stacksteads Silver Band. They then dance their way through the streets of Bacup. There are a number of theories behind their outlandish appearance. One view is that it's a reference to their pagan roots. Another is that it is to do with their mining background. Whatever the truth, the Coconut Dancers are a famous Lancashire custom! While this is a particularly famous aspect of folk culture within the county, folk dance and song are both long-standing traditions throughout the whole of Lancashire.

Lancashire Day - 27th November

All part of the show:
the textile trades assembly point at the 1902 Preston Guild

Lancashire Day

The 27th of November is officially Lancashire Day. It's an occasion when Lancashire people celebrate their county, marked by special events and town criers reading out the Lancashire Day proclamation across the county. Lancashire Day marks the day in 1295 when Lancashire sent its first representatives to the Parliament of King Edward I of England to attend what went on to become known as The Model Parliament. It was first observed in 1996 with the loyal toast to 'The Queen, Duke of Lancaster'.

The Preston Guild: England's oldest festival

When people in Lancashire say that something happens only 'once every Preston Guild', they're referring to a real tradition. The saying refers to an ancient custom which is well and truly alive in Lancashire today. The Preston Guild is a major festival which takes place only every 20 years. The tradition was started in 1542 to showcase the talents of guild merchants after Henry II granted Preston its first royal charter and established a Guild Merchant in 1179. Nowadays, the Preston Guild is a major event with street parties and firework displays which attracts thousands of visitors and appearances from many local traders and businesses!

An area of outstanding natural beauty:
The forest of Bowland in Lancashire. Shutterstock ©Kevin Eaves.

Say what? Surprising facts about Lancashire

- Lancashire covers an area of 1,189 square miles (3,075 sq km), making it one of the largest shire counties.

- Despite Lancashire's long industrial past, 80 per cent of the county is officially classed as rural.

- Lancashire is the home of the very centre of the British Isles – Dunsop Bridge in the Ribble Valley.

The blue plaque (at the Iffley Road sports ground in Oxford) which marks **Roger Bannister's** important achievement.

Copyright: Martin Anderson

A taste of Lancashire

Lancashire is known for its delicious dishes, both past and present. Read on to discover what people of the region enjoyed eating – some of which are remain firmly on the menu!

Courting Cakes

The Lancashire Courting Cake combined flirting with food in a unique way. It was the custom by which a woman would create a special cake to give to her fiancé to show her affection. While the cake was filled with jam in the colder months (either raspberry or strawberry with a shortbread base), in summer it was packed with fresh strawberries or raspberries.

'Arise, Sir Loin!'

Do you like a nice piece of sirloin steak? Then you might be interested to know that Lancashire is where this particular cut of meat was first named. The story is that when King James I was staying at Hoghton Tower in 1617, he was having such a good time that one night while having dinner, he drew his sword and knighted the beef, saying the immortal words, *'Arise Sir Loin'*.

Sirloin steak: food fit for a king!
Shutterstock ©Kesu

Lancashire hotpot, straight from the oven!
Shutterstock ©Joe Gough

Lancashire Hotpot

We've all heard of Lancashire Hotpot. But what is actually in this famous Northern meal? Traditionally a hotpot would be made from either lamb or mutton with onion and covered with sliced potatoes. It would have been created in a very tall and large brown pot. The custom was taken to the next level in October 2007 when what is the world's biggest hotpot to date (weighing in at 200kg) was made in Garstang as part of the launch of Taste Lancashire 08!

Butter pie

Butter pie is another firm Lancashire favourite. Despite the name, it's not made from butter, but from onions and potatoes!

Hoghton Tower

Black pudding

This is a favourite in Lancashire and also a key feature in the annual Black Pudding World Championships, mentioned elsewhere in this book!

Wet Nelly

Wet Nelly is another dish with an intriguing name. A popular Lancashire pudding, Wet Nelly was a clever way to make leftovers go further by using up stale cakes and leftover scraps of pastry and adding an egg custard base.

Chorley cake

Chorley cakes (or Fly Pie, as they're sometimes known

locally) are a close relation of the Eccles cake, but are of course closely linked to Chorley in Lancashire. These shortcrust pastry cakes filled with currants and raisins are not as sweet as Eccles cakes. They're often enjoyed with a little butter or some cheese.

Lancashire cheese

This delicious locally made cheese comes in three varieties, from Creamy Lancashire and mature Tasty Lancashire made using a traditional approach to Crumbly Lancashire (known locally as Lancashire Crumbly within Lancashire) which is made using more modern techniques.

Parkin

When you combine oatmeal and black treacle the right way, you end up with Parkin (also known as Perkin). While this delicious cake does not originate in Lancashire, it is extremely popular with local residents. What distinguishes Lanky Parkin from other kinds is the fact that it is made with golden syrup instead of treacle and with a higher volume of sugar.

Tripe and onions

It is thought that Lancashire is where tripe and onions first originated. While it may not appeal to everyone these days, it was a cheap and sustaining dish many years ago.

Barm Cakes

This Lancashire staple is actually a bap or bread roll which is created using wholemeal flour. In Lancashire dialect, 'Barm' refers to the froth on liquid that contains yeast. Barm cakes were a great accompaniment to all kinds of meals.

Manchester Tart

Also known as Manchester Pudding, this traditional baked tart combines a shortcrust pastry shell filled with custard, a layer of raspberry jam with flaked coconut and a maraschino cherry on top. Delicious!

Acknowledgements

I would like to thank Lancashire Archives and the Lancashire Record Office for their help with my research for this book and for the use of photographs from their collections.

Lancashire Lantern Image Archive –
http://lanternimages.lancashire.gov.uk

THE EXISTENTIAL CLUB

THE
EXISTENTIAL
CLUB

SHAYAAN REHMAN

White Falcon
Publishing

www.whitefalconpublishing.com

The Existential Club
Shayaan Rehman

www.whitefalconpublishing.com

Requests for permission should be addressed to
rehmanshayaan@gmail.com

ISBN - 978-1-63640-654-1

Persistence

- John L. Seagull

We have our roles
And all play necessary games

Go through the ritual
That is mankind, life, dust

Impossible particles of space
Time beyond and through

We dance our eternal dance
Of coming closer
Taking distance

But persistence

The Existential Club

My dear friend
Will lead us
To the undeniable end
Of material existence
Giving us
The opportunity
To fly free

Into the deep depth
Of the greatest question

Hunting you and me.

Contents

The Highway

Cohle raced his jet black 1969 Camaro SS through a long and winding highway that had empty farms on both sides and few fellow vehicles. Life had been very good for him, everything always managing to work out in the end for him; he had everything a man from the outside could envy, a decent place to live, good health and a pretty slick ride. He worked at a corporate law firm and had done very well for himself moving through the ranks of the corporate web to make a commendable living.

Everything was perfect and all was good, Cohle thought. After all he had everything society would ever expect a man to have and yet somehow Cohle felt far from being complete, no matter how grand life got there was this looming feeling of something being amiss deep down, like a part of him being empty.

At times he wondered if this feeling was something that all men had a conflict with and he dwelled upon the many he ways he had tried to make up for it, work had made for a fine anesthesia initially however as time flew by he realized that after a certain point it was nothing more but an empty pursuit.

A couple of years ago he had been under the impression that the missing part in his life was in fact a suitable partner, a soul mate, a lover. Even the bare thought about the concept made Cohle grin quite cynically.

He didn't always feel this way; his first relationship did make him feel complete, like it was the answer to everything missing in life, true and everlasting happiness always seemed an arm's reach away, he reminisced fondly about the only girl he'd been serious with, a lovely design student from Georgia, Cohle's eye gleamed as the rays from the headlights of a passing car going towards his rear hit him, it was dusk by now on a cold December making the visibility a bit low.

His thoughts dwelled on Anni; he'd met her on a short solo vacation, one of many he used to take after getting newly settled and thriving at work. This particular vacation had been to Italy. Anni was in town with college friends after graduation; their chance meeting took place on a Wednesday night at the La Cabala club in Rome;

On that particular night she had been sitting alone on a table for four people, Cohle saw her and wondered why this lovely girl with streaked brown hair was enjoying her drinks in solitude even though she looked like a tourist.

He approached her with a polite smile and asked her if she was alone, she smiled back and blurted out something along the lines of how her friends had been too tired and were back to the hotel room and then to Cohle's delight asked him to join her and he gladly accepted.

They instantly connected, sat down at the same table for three hours or more, time spent with her seemed to just fly by for Cohle, everything felt exalting in her presence, this was very rare for him, and they had some drinks, danced for a while, and however eventually called it quits after almost blacking out on the floor. The crowd was leaving and the music was going down by now, Cohle looked at Anni and thought it was now or never to be with a wonderful girl like her, his mind raced to figure out a way to spend just a single moment more with her.

Back to the highway now, Cohle shivered as he turned the heating on, he felt cold, perhaps it was from all the reminiscing but he got rid of that illogical thought, it's just chilly outside he exclaimed to himself and kept on driving, he had a long way to go and the road just stretched on. Yet he zoned out soon and his mind went back towards Anni;

Looking at her radiant face back in the club he approached her with an unusually nervous stride and asked her if he was going to see her again, "why of course, I'm still in town for a couple of days, I'd like to see you again" she said with a smile. Cohle felt like the most reassured man on the earth and they parted ways for that night.

The once chance meeting had eventually spiraled into a full blown relationship, they had spent the remainder of their vacation in Italy together, exploring the city squares, sitting in cafes for hours and just being with each other. It wasn't long after getting back to their countries that they longed to see each other more and so began their plans to travel together.

Cohle and Anni would met each other in Switzerland next, something that was planned during their time Italy itself and they had spent a week backpacking across the country with its scenic valleys and fjords.

It had been quite a remarkable adventure; they were like two outlaws without a care for the rest of their worlds in the moments that they shared together, traversing the beautiful landscapes with none but each other on their side.

That trip had been however cut short by some bad news, Anni's younger sister had fallen ill and she needed to be there, Cohle completely understood and joined her back at the airport before leaving back home as well.

The months flew by and everything was better again. Anni came to meet him in his country not too long after landing her first job and they celebrated it together, she stayed with him for a week and they'd connected even more. He'd take her to all the amazing places he knew around home and anywhere she'd like, everything was incredible.

On Anni's last night before flying back they were having an early dinner together at his place and their conversation became a little philosophical, courtesy of the bottle of merlot accompanying their meal;

"Are we in love?" Anni asked cheekily. "That depends; I suppose what does the word even mean?" Cohle said.

Anni laughed, "Are we going to debate semantics today then, is that it?" They both burst into laughter.

"That's exactly what we're doing tonight then, why don't you go first and give me your definition of love?"

"Mhmm for me I guess it's having a genuine connection with someone"

"Geez, I expected that clichéd answer from you"

Anni laughed and hit his arm, "Okay in that case, why don't you give me your insightful answer on the question of the meaning of love?"

"Very well then, for me it's being with someone who is tolerable enough to spend a considerable time with, that's what, makes a suitable partner, someone you feel comfortable sharing your personal space with"

"Woah that actually makes a lot of sense when you think about it, so a relationship's essentially like having a co-pilot to your life"

"Damn, you had to make that sound clichéd too huh?" Cohle said cheekily

"Of course, It is one of my talents you see"
Anni smiled moved closer to embrace him.

"I love you princess"Cohle placed his arm
around her shoulder

"Yeah who's the clichéd one now? Well I love
you too Cohle" Everything in that moment was
so beautiful; he wished it would never end.

Empty words; Cohle thought now by
himself as he came back to the overcast
present, driving through the wide highway
lanes across the derelict land. For that had
been the last time he'd seen Anni before
she flew back home. After that she'd just
disappeared from his life, no calls, no texts;
radio silence, there was no way for him to
reach out to her.

She was gone and she had apparently
abandoned him without saying why, back
then it had been a difficult time for Cohle,
her leaving him in the way she did left him
yearning for her but also with all kinds of
tearing questions as to why she wasn't with
him anymore; perhaps he was not enough,
perhaps she had found someone better than

him, perhaps she never loved him in the first place and all of what they had was nothing but a short lived phase, a lie that Cohle had perceived to be true.

Most likely she saw him for someone that he wasn't and soon as she came around to really knowing and understanding him she realized he wasn't that someone and ghosted him right from there. *So many explanations and such little closure*, he thought.

What was all of it even for, he wondered, all that time, those feelings he saw as love, all for nothing. *Maybe people just don't fall in love with each other; they fall in love with ideas and abstractions.*

Regardless the whole business with Anni changed him profoundly as a person, The resentfulness caused him to become someone he wasn't previously; he began seeing attachments as unnecessary and preferred to stay a cold person, walking over anyone's sentiments as he saw fit. After all he didn't believe in the idea of love, why should he abide by its rules.

In the following years Cohle's personality developed into a Stoic and Casanova like character, he'd charm a girl with a shiny smile and his reassuring words that were comparable to a rehearsed script to the point she'd start believing him to be the one for her without a second thought, yet soon as he got bored he would cut her off and leave.

This cycle had been going on for a while now, it became almost thrilling for him, winning a girl over and breaking up after finding the next one, to him that was only fair, he had gone through the same thing, why shouldn't the others. The whole process was immensely satisfying for him and he didn't care about the girls he left behind.

Nobody meant anything for him, the way he saw it, everything was a game, you win or you lose, and he liked winning. From his work in the corporate world to his personal relationships he was always calculated and cold in his approach, Cohle believed that this gave him an edge over others in the kind of world that he lived in.

His overly indifferent demeanor prevented him from forming any kind of intimate or lasting relationship with people, every person in the world was like a piece from a game for him, to use and discard as he saw fit.

That's all that life was for him anymore, it wasn't some glorified journey, full of adventures and long lasting relationships, for him it was just a simple game, a game where he must always come out on top, Cohle didn't care much to take pleasure in his daily life, in fact he didn't feel much of anything anymore.

He looked towards the roads and its horizons, it had started to rain lightly and the evening road glimmered with raindrops falling from the dusky sky while fields of green stretched far on either side of the highway. A view that a previous Cohle would've appreciated greatly although this one was simply indifferent to it all, an unchanging road to get where we wanted to was all he could think of it and he drove on faster. Little had sparked joy in him after Anni, everything felt mundane and new things and events didn't excite him like they should have. *Time moves forward and nothing changes.*

The car dashed through the wet road, it was getting dark and the rain was falling much heavily now, a storm was coming, Cohle didn't bother and continued to accelerate at his usual pace. The highway appeared to be deserted now and it was just him for miles.

He zoned out while driving, not even realizing how much distance he'd covered, unnoticed by him a truck approached on the other side right opposite to him, the truck driver, an overworked fella being under the impression that the road was empty and wanting to get to his destination soon as he could, never saw the car across him, by the time Cohle saw the blinding headlights of the truck right in front of him it was too late for to hit the brakes, he turned the steering with a jerk making the car skid off road and crash into an electric pole. Suddenly everything went dim.

***

Cohle's eyes moved in and out of consciousness, black was all he could see and a ringing silence was all he heard, he didn't feel any kind of pain much to his surprise and managed to push himself out of the car, it was cold and wet outside but he dragged his feet and walked away from the car soon as he could, he needed to stop a passerby car immediately and get help, he took long strides and walked forward in the heavy rain along a seemingly never-ending highway when he saw something that made him freeze right in his tracks.

Standing right across him was a familiar looking girl, he recognized her brown streaked hair and semi tanned face even in the dark night, Anni stood across him and looked him in the eyes. Cohle had never felt so confused before, all of it felt so surreal, his mind couldn't comprehend what was happening and he just looked at her without saying a word, he had no idea where to start.

"Anni?" he managed to blurt out.

The girl just kept staring at him while giving him a gentle nod.

"Is it really you, say something" Cohle said.

"Who else would it be?" Anni finally broke her silence and smiled at him.

"I missed you, so much"

"I know, I missed you too Cohle"

Cohle felt fragile and vulnerable as all of the emotions came pouring in; joy, fear, longing, grief. He glanced at the soaking asphalt and looked up at her again. "Why, why did you have to leave me like that Anni?"

"I never wanted to leave you, it wasn't my choice, I need you to understand that" her eyes showed a hint of melancholy

"Nothing was the same without you, all these years, where have you been, you never contacted me after going back home?"

Anni moved closer to him, Cohle noticed something off about her appearance but couldn't quite put a finger on it; something was quite strange about the two of them standing close in the pouring rain and holding this conversation, all of it felt so dreamlike.

"I never made it back home Cohle"

"What do you mean?" he couldn't understand anything now, nothing made sense.

"Don't you understand? I was on my way home, and just two miles away from home a public bus rammed into the taxi I was in, I didn't pull through."

"You didn't survive?" Cohle asked uneasily

Anni's face showed a great sadness, "I didn't, I died on the spot".

He couldn't believe her, "How exactly are you here now then?"

"I had to be here for you in this moment; it wouldn't have made sense if it was someone else right now"

"Why, what's so important about this moment? How are you even here if you died all these years ago?"

"There's a good reason you can see me, and why we're speaking right now"

Cohle felt his hands beginning to tremble, and his breathing became heavy, "And what is it?"

"Are you really ready to hear it?"

"Just tell me Anni"

"Cohle, you just died"

"What? No I didn't I'm right here standing on my legs"

"I'm here too; you wouldn't be seeing me if you were still alive, you were in an accident, just like I was back then"

"No, this cannot be, am I dreaming?" his heart raced as he sought to make sense of the situation.

"You're in denial, I get it, but you need to face the fact that you're not alive anymore Cohle"

"But I got out, I made it out of the car by myself, I walked all this way and then I saw you, I cannot be dead"

"You never got out of the car Cohle" she said with a calm tone

He felt tears beginning to form in his eyes as the reality of the situation started creeping in, with a heavy heart he reluctantly turned around to look back at his car and see for himself.

There he was, still lying in the driver's seat with a lifeless face; Cohle saw his own corpse and broke down. This was unbelievable, he had so much more to do in life, he was nowhere close to the things he'd wanted to do and so many things he wanted to feel. "So this is it for me then, why are you here?"

"I needed to tell you Cohle, I never left you, you had to know the reason why I was gone, I loved you and I still do and I wish things had turned out differently, waiting to let you know has been very painful"

"I wasn't the best of a person Anni, you not being here changed me, for the worse I'm afraid, I have been a terrible human being and now it's all over" he was trembling as he uttered this final self-realization.

Anni inched closer and embraced him, "I know, don't worry everything will be okay, death is not the end and it's beautiful out there"

"Out where?"

"It wouldn't be my place to tell you that, that's something you'll experience for yourself but we'll be together dear"

The thought of being with her did provide him significant comfort but the unfulfilled nature of his life came back creeping to him again, "it's not fair Anni, I need to go back, there's so much I did wrong, so many people I did wrong, I'll never get to make it right".

"Sometimes we don't get to make it right, life just happens and you don't get to choose when it ends, it just does, you did what you did, there's no changing that"

"I'm not talking about changing it all, but the least I could do is try and repair a bit of all that damage, all that pain I've caused, it's all I ask for"

"I understand your need for closure, but you need to accept what's done is done, wouldn't you rather just be with me now"

"I'll wait a whole lifetime just to be with you again, but I want to get back and have another chance at my life, I have to do some things differently, my story cannot be over like this"

Anni glanced sympathetically at him, the two of them stood silently for a while in the rainy night against the backdrop of a crashed car "Do you really want that, to go back?"

"I do Anni, although I'm not sure that's possible now" he looked on with a determined and rigid expression.

"It might as well be possible, for you" Anni shook her head back towards his car, Cohle took a step back to get a clear view of himself lying on the car seat, his body now appeared to be twitching slightly, perhaps he wasn't quite gone yet. Cohle sensed things starting to feel blurry, "Will I see you again? If I go back right now"

She placed her hand on his shoulder to comfort him, "You will. Though I guess we'll have to wait another lifetime to be together again, goodbye Cohle and good luck" she said with a self-assured smile.

Cohle felt even hazier now and his movements became heavy, as if he was being drawn back into something against his control, with as much energy he could use to resist it he inched further and embraced Anni for a final time, until everything went grey.

***

Sunlight drizzled in through the cracked windshield waking Cohle up out of unconsciousness, the night had given away by now and the rainfall had stopped. He pushed the door open carefully and stepped out of the car, after taking a quick glance at the driver's seat he moved towards the other side to stop any passerby that would come this way.

For a moment he stopped to look around his surroundings, the fields bordering the highway looked greener than ever, the clouds creeping away; it was going to be a sunny day he thought looking up at the clear blue skies.

The warmth of the sun soothed him and the road looked beautiful; stretching straight far across the horizon. He was now aware of every single thing he was going to do differently this time and set things right, after all not everyone gets to have a second shot and he was going to live a life as meaningful as he could make it, and in the end he'd be back with the girl he loves.

Cohle heard a distant rumbling noise of a car engine which felt like music to his ears at this point and he spotted a minivan heading his way, he moved towards the middle of the road with a cheery expression and his thumb out, everything was perfect and all was good.

The Radio

"Ignorance is bliss"

Many years it had been, many fine years since Flemico radio had first broadcasted. Back in the previous days it had been nothing much but a simple morning slot radio channel booming through the monotonous rides of folks going about their lives. It was owned by a moderately successful newspaper publisher seeking to expand his reach, reading was rapidly becoming a thing of the past.

The content back then was usually centered on local happenings, entertainment et cetera without much care for the wider world around; it existed as an entity separated from the peripheral world with programs about close-by sports events, the odd piece of news every now and then as well as some overworked banter.

People would tune in to the station and ride to their places of work, homes or to other unspecified destinations, it was a free world after all. People could move around freely, speak freely and live freely, not too long ago as unlikely as that sounds, just 20 years.

The world had changed drastically in the last twenty years, even back then government surveillance existed but it wasn't as overt as it is now with the bio-metric based citizen register or the militarized police or government checkpoints at every other turn of the road. Perhaps the most surprising feature of the previous world which now been long gone was that any individual could go to the internet, the internet was something one could think of as a network of different computers across the world, accessible by anyone and communicate anything they had in mind. They shut it down 8 years back citing the prevalence of countless loopholes one could use in using it despite their regulations.

They ran the world now; oligarchies, autocracies and the deep states. Every single country on the planet had fallen into their hands, the process of course had been started long ago before it became so obvious and by the time people realized what was happening it had already happened. The country didn't matter of course, tyranny hides among many different shades and liberty as a concept had been slowly vanquished, in fact the new citizens liked their police states, the vast majority at least.

Back to flemico now, the radio channel wasn't a simple local radio station anymore with the radio hosts chatting about weekly football matches and so on. It had since fallen into decrepit. Its equipment and frequency had been taken over and adopted by an underground radio station with unknown operators, the name remain unchanged yet the content differed now, the talks on the channel told people how the world they think they know used to be and how things had changed in the prior years. The underground radio ironically got more popular than it originally ever was. It enjoyed a rather global audience, something that was never anticipated by the new operators.

No one knew who these new operators were, according to some the station was nothing more than a government ruse, designed to weed out any non-conformists or deviants, others believed it to be the real deal. The radio hosts themselves remained vague calling themselves the narrators with there being two of them; the first narrator and the second. The station had gotten quite popular due to the mere curiosity of people when faced with a narrative that's different to the things they grow up believing as well as the fact that there wasn't an internet anymore.

The state as immense in its power as it was couldn't trace the operators and in short didn't really care about them considering it to be below their level of concern. This was in spite of the station openly challenging their entire foundation, the state believed in its supremacy and seeing a meager radio station as a threat would challenge its narrative of absolute control.

The radio of a lone car parked on an isolated highway roared to life, far away from the towering skyscrapers and watchful eyes the passengers often travelled to this spot so they could listen to flemico radio in peace. Listening to it with the wrong ears nearby had the possibility of attracting unwarranted attention, as they lit up a single cigarette to share among themselves they heard the familiar voice of the hosts.

"Hello there, good morning people and welcome once again to flemico radio, this is me and my co-host and we've got a bit to talk about today so let's dive right in, we've had several questions, time to answer them" said thefirst narrator.

"How about this; For starters, we've got a lot of calls asking us if we're revolutionaries, we're not" the second narrator said.

"You got that right; there are no revolutionaries, not anymore".

"Aye brother, that ship sure has sailed".

"We're just a voice, talking about a world people have forgotten"

The second narrator paused at this sentence, looked around the studio for a while, revolution was a fantasy, they weren't revolutionaries, just two people in a hastily constructed studio which had to change locations every now and then.

"Just a voice, you're absolutely correct, speaking of voice we've got a lot of questions from our audience written down here, let the answering commence!"

It was common practice for the station to receive questions occasionally and answer them the first question scribble on the yellowed pages of a large notepad was; *why didn't the people back then rise up against totalitarianism?*The *second narrator read it out.*

"Well, in a nutshell back then people were so caught up in the your team, my team absurdity they forgot to call out wrong when it didn't fit into their narrative, selective outrage got so common, it became a norm

In the society of ours, the introduction of this culture enabled the regimes to use figureheads on both ends of the stick and steadily advance their influence and you know the rest of the story".

"Not to mention the manipulation carried out through mass media campaigns that subverted people's opinions without them ever finding out."

The two men glanced at each other for a brief moment, it was quite a good explanation, the first narrator moved on to the second question written on the notepad; *aren't we living in a much more peaceful world now?*, he read the question out.

"Peace? What they tell you about peace today is nothing but an illusion, a mask. More people die every day; entire nations go to war more now than ever, you just don't find out. There is no peace; rather violence has become the norm now that the states are so powerful".

"Speaking of which does anyone know the CCP bombed down an American frigate this morning, claimed it was in Chinese waters, the US president has ordered heavy retaliation. You see folks, the media does not report conflict anymore, and it's just so commonplace now."

"Indeed, anyways back to the question the world was much more peaceful back then, democracy kept the governments in check, there were independent global institutions and the internet allowed everyone to inform the rest of the world what was happening, that's in the past now".

The next question was a relatively new, people didn't care anymore to ask them that, the narrators browsed the notepad; *what's the purpose behind this channel?*

The purpose, the narrators thought to themselves, sure they could say that they were fighting against ignorance and tyranny. That they were some sort of romanticized underdogs facing down the leviathan that the state was, embers burning through the night. Yet deep down they didn't see themselves as heroes, they were simply broadcasting simple truths hidden in plain sight, they weren't fighters or rebels, just journalists. To consider themselves as heroes would be a colossal exaggeration of their obligations to the world.

"The purpose, Well we simply try to show people the straight truths so that they can think for themselves instead of being led on" the 1st narrator said after reading aloud the question.

"That, I believe sums up our purpose, we filter the relevant truths from a vast overflow of information and try to dedicatedly deliver them to our listeners".

It was the partial truth, they did simply present information which was already out there. What they didn't confide to their audience was the fact that they did in fact have a few sources in the upper echelons of governance, people who found themselves on the other side of the line, believers of freedom and liberty who had no choice but join the forces they despised. Conformity was a stairway to power,privilege and security; resistance would have had severe consequences.

These individuals were rare, the majority had accepted the status that came with their power and didn't care for any ideals, and this creeping normalization had been the same everywhere. The sources were useful in acquiring instant and verified information, something which had become exceptional in today's time.

News of cyber-attacks, air raids, armed conflict reached them at the earliest, completely sieved from all the unnecessary and irrelevant information that the media was flooded with. These sources were mainly people the operators had known from back in the days when they themselves had worked for government intelligence. Their service years were brief and they had left the intermediate level, becoming disillusioned with the state and all, most of the others remained and found their way slightly up the ladder.

***

Meanwhile, on the other side of the world there was an atmosphere of uncertainty and apprehension aboard a lone Ohio class submarine of the United States navy as it lay three hundred meters below the surface of the South China Sea. The crew had now been aware that one of their ships had been downed, they argued among themselves in hustled tones of the possible outcomes they could be headed to. The submarine was equipped with nuclear warheads, generally meant to serve as simple deterrence as it always had. The situation was a bit complicated now; they were the closest to Chinese mainland and had the paramount range to strike the Chinese, should the order for the attack come through.

Captain O'connel stood across from executive officer Lelacey, the order to prepare for launch had actually come through 10 minutes ago, and the two men looked at each other with silent contemplation, they both knew what the beginning of the launch would bring about, the chain of events that would be set off by launching the nuke.

The men had their reluctance and doubts, but they were good soldiers and good soldiers follow orders. The wording of the order was perfect and they knew what needed to be done.

The captain and the executive officer then took turns to announce order the launch over the general announcing system respectively, it was time. O'connel turned over the keys required to initiate the missile launch tubes, it wasn't something he wanted to do but he didn't budge while doing so, orders were orders. The procedure to launch the nukes was put into motion.

***

Back at the radio station the narrators were cooped up in their respective chairs, it was their smoking break and they sat in silent contemplation, cigarettes in hand. Their work was stressful at times, talking about the harsh realities of the contemporary world, reporting on atrocious incidents throughout the day, all of that starts to get to a man's head after a while.

Everything was calm and peaceful in the room surrounded by a multitude of equipment when suddenly almost all of the said equipment started sounding off and beeping; every kind of alarm went off.

"What in the actual hell, Check this out" the first narrator said as he pulled his chair towards the nearest computer system, the ballistic missile detector had been activated and it was going crazy, it showed the virtual map swarming with launched missiles.

"Wait this cannot be accurate, these are too many nukes and they're flying everywhere, this has to wrong." The second narrator replied.

He started go through the other equipment.

Meanwhile the first narrator was staring at his phone, the confirmation for their fears had come, and it was all real.

"I'm afraid it's not brother, this is happening" he said with a faltering tone. It had all happened too abruptly, everyone had launched whatever deterrence they had towards each other, all it took was someone to take the first shot and now too many nukes were in the sky and time was running out.

"They are not telling anyone, look at the fucking news sources, all of them, there's not even a mention of this, the people won't even know".

"Well it's our bloody job then to tell them, they need to know!"

"I don't think anyone is going to make out of this alive, the fallout would be too large, it is going to annihilate everything, the rate at which the missiles are headed we have what two hours give or take?"

"Hurry up, let's get the radio back on, we need to announce this now".

The second narrator didn't respond and rather looked at him with a yielding expression.

The first narrator shook his shoulders, "we should get started, what are you even thinking about right now?"

"I'm thinking, what's even the point?"

"For what?" said the first narrator.

"What's the point of telling everyone that the end is here, that the entirety of their lives would be over within two hours or less, that this is it for everyone" the second narrator said.

"It's our duty, we've been sharing all these awful news for I don't even remember how many years, and we need to report this too so common, let's go on about it".

"No, we don't need to announce this, sure this is our obligation but I don't believe it's the best thing to do now, the way I see it these folks are probably living their last moments, what good can possibly come out of torturing them with the knowledge of something they cannot change."

"This is a huge decision, the mainstream media outlets sure as hell won't tell the people, we should at least give them a heads up".

"Nothing good will come from it brother, what's done is done. The least we could do is let these people live the remainder of their lives without the fear of their impending doom, you need to understand".

"So we just let these people die out of the blue?"

"They're going to die either way, its only mercy if we don't let them know".

"So what are we going to do? Just go live with our show again and act as if everything's fine".

"I believe that's exactly what we should do, one last show, that's all we can do at this point, it's the role we get to play." The second narrator said.

The first narrator reluctantly started to set up and prepared to go back online again, he was aided by the second narrator and soon enough they were ready.

They started to speak.

"Good evening everybody from me and my co-host, it's a beautiful day we're having today…

***

This time they had a strangely uplifting show, their best one to date, nothing about politics or wars or strikes or brutal governments, just a simple one about trivial facts, entertainment and some sports, much like in the good old days.

Between splits in their words they did wonder about what they were doing as everything was coming to an end and the curtains were about to close, they silently questioned the meaning of it all between pauses but eventually shrugged off all those thoughts, didn't matter much now either.

The first narrator's mind dwelled on a few things; the world they had known so far wasn't perfect but it had its redeeming aspects, *we had some good people, books, works of art, coffee, mountains, beaches, the list could go on and on.*He came to terms with the end of the beautiful world he had been privileged to be a part off and continued with the show.

They even started taking song requests towards the end of the show and as they put on the top ten much requested songs they retired back to their chairs, listened to the cheerful beats blaring in their headphones, they closed their eyes and waited. The nukes were flying and soon enough, all off it would be over.

The Astronaut

The spacecraft Sagan-V voyaged through deep space, its occupant being a lone astronaut long slumbering, the spacecraft's functions were largely automated, powered with nuclear fission technology the craft was rather one of its kind. The previous iterations and the prototypes hadn't been very successful and didn't manage to survive in space for a long time but Sagan-V was truly a human wonder. It had been successful in carrying a human the furthest from earth and was still going strong.

It was white and metallic colored on the exterior, with an almost stream-lined cone shaped chassis that had multiple thrusters on the side. The living quarters were rather small as the only passenger had been on cryogenic sleep; the only way he could survive for the extensive duration of the journey.

The reason for this expedition was a series of radio signals received simultaneously by almost all stations that had sent out their own transmissions into the depths of outer space in the hope of receiving a response from or at least a trace from intelligent life. The received signals didn't have any message save for a set of coordinates to a specific planet orbiting a star system, and that is exactly where the Sagan-V was headed.

It hadn't been easy none of it; securing the funds, designing and constructing the top notch spacecraft, bringing several nations together or even finding the suitable individual who'd be representing all of humanity as a whole; a single human being travelling a long way from home in the hopes of finding possibly, a new one along with new neighbors. It had taken lots of determination from many individuals having the right amount of confidence in global solidarity in trying times like those, but at the end all had of that had proved to be fruitful as Sagan-V was complete, launched with its passenger and was on the verge of reaching its destination.

The passenger, slumbering in cryo-sleep was major Emin, born and brought up in the states after his family migrated from Germany, he had done very well for himself as an air-force pilot and was a man of few faults. He was a simple gent, a bachelor as he never quite believed in the idea of relationships or marriage but was nonetheless known to people as a reliable and warm person.

Major Emin had been interviewed and evaluated by representatives of several nations, only after which his selection for the mission had been agreed upon and confirmed, he had proven himself suitable for the mission without quarrel, something that was quite a feat among itself, being a person everyone can be on common ground with. That's what made major Emin the perfect candidate for being the astronaut aboard the Sagan-V.

The capsule in which he was asleep was pure white and complete with various screens checking up on his vitals along with all support systems required to keep him alive and breathing. The temperature inside was set to -196 degree Celsius to ensure an almost complete halt to the aging process and the capsule was designed to revive him from cryo-sleep soon as the craft reached its destination. Around the capsule was the craft's main control screen, communication systems as well as a sturdy space suit ready for the astronaut to put on and venture onto the surface. On the craft wall there was a tiny round window which would allow a glance at the galaxy in all its glory of more than a billion stars illuminating the endless night.

***

A rapid beeping sound broke the silence inside the craft, all the machinations of the capsule went to work, Sagan-V had found its way to the destination and it was time to wake up. The capsule whirred open and the astronaut opened his eyes, everything was blurry and white, for a moment he felt he was back in the comforts of home, just awoken from an afternoon nap, back on earth with golden sunlight piercing through his eyelids, yet as the reality of the present situation settled in gradually Emin didn't delay in springing straight into action and got himself up.

His spacesuit and gear was ready in front of him, the control system awaited him to commence the auto-landing sequence, and he strode towards it and initiated the sequence to begin.

The craft approached the atmosphere and initiated it's descent to the surface while tilting itself and maintaining the correct angle so as to not abruptly end the long journey it had made to get here. Emin looked through the window and he could make out the view of the planet outside; he saw an endless continent that was entirely black on the surface and striped throughout with huge grayish mountain ranges, the sky was filled with dark clouds and there was an overbearing deep blue light from the star smothering the planet, all of this made for the planet to feel quite overwhelming for him.

With the support of thrusters on the sides of the craft, it landed on the ground and went into the post landing sequence to ensure it would stand strong on the terrain. Major Emin's gear had a wearable navigation device that looked similar to a wearable mini-tablet which was embedded with the coordinates that had been received at home; it was accurate to a hundred yards and would lead him to the exact source from where they had come from.

Having put the spacesuit on, complete with all his gear Emin looked at the navigation screen, on his forearm now and opened the hatch to climb down to the ground.

Without having much of a look around he climbed down the extendable ladder going down to the surface and once he made it to the last step Emin turned and looked around; He felt a strange overwhelming emotion from seeing the vastness of the planet around him, he saw a mountain range close by that was at least thrice the size of any mountain back on earth, the sky was dark and the light coming from the star was nowhere close to sunlight, it glowed eerily across the horizon with bluish rays piercing through the black clouds.

The coordinates were pointing towards the mountain ranges in the west; the astronaut took a long look around the immense emptiness and started walking forward. As he inched closer to his destination, step by step his thoughts dwelled on the purpose of his mission and its importance in the grand scale of things, he'd been sent as the lone seeker of answers that more than seven billion of his kind wanted to; about the universe, their place in it and if there was anything more out there.

Sure enough when he returned from this expedition everyone he ever personally knew will be all but gone forever, it might be that he'd be returning to an earth that would be far different from the one he had left behind and knew so well; all of these feelings ran around his head only to be drowned out by the sheer anticipation of what lied ahead, what the coordinates would lead him to.

He wondered about their source, where had they come from? Looking around he saw no signs of life, just the immense emptiness, *no friends but the mountains.*

The astronaut's navy blue spacesuit blended in seamlessly with the deep blue atmosphere of the planet camouflaging him to his surroundings like he was an inherent part of the terrain; an estranged man finally back where he belonged.

He glanced throughout the horizon, looking for movement or a sign of life yet all he saw was absolute calm and nothingness, perhaps the whole expedition was a huge blunder, he thought. Coming all this way to discover more of what was out there and only to find that there was in fact nothing else much would be awfully disappointing. He carried on.

***

The mountains were much closer and Emin could make out their enormous altitude now, they were gigantic; soaring grey peaks going all the way up to the skies, they made him feel uneasy and inconsequential as if he was but a speck of dust in the grand scale of the cosmos. Navigation indicated the coordinates to be quite close, leading straight towards the base of the mountains, he felt confused as to where he was supposed to reach and what would he find in the midst of a mountain range millions of miles away from home.

Emin questioned the nature of what the coordinates were supposed to mean, whether they were an invitation, seeking out humanity to finally come out of its crutches and move on towards the rest of the universe or some kind of message hopefully providing them some answers that humankind had always yearned to seek. He could feel his heart beat and breathing get faster as he inched closer to his destination, the eagerness and curiosity was getting to him.

About two hundred yards from the foot of the mountain that navigation was leading to him the astronaut didn't dare look upward for the overwhelming sight of the summit could be too much for him in that moment, instead he walked more and more briskly moving soil that most likely hadn't changed its position since the previous thousand years.

At the base of the enormous mountain he saw an opening right where the coordinates were supposed to be and walked closer to get a proper glance, it looked like an entrance to cave but getting nearby there appeared to be a peculiar glimmer on its surface like a darkened pool of water, finally being face to face with the opening he saw what appeared to be a glimmering mirror-like exterior which reflected everything around the planet except for the astronaut himself.

Emin was utterly confused about the nature of the structure that he saw in front of him, he put his hand forward reprehensively and it went right to the other side as if he had dipped it in a lake. Taking a long sigh he walked across it and everything went white for half a second.

Coming back to senses he found himself inside a vast and deep cavern that was surrounded by a pale luminescent glow going all the way up to a top he couldn't see. He walked straight ahead and suddenly felt the presence of something else sharing the space with him, in his peripheral he saw a figure coming up behind his right, Emin froze in his tracks, his heart raced and he felt an adrenaline rush coursing through his body, getting the courage, he turned around to face the figure.

***

It was an old man standing across him, a human.

"Major Emin, I see you've finally arrived, it's alright you can remove the helm, no one can die in this place" The old man said.

The astronaut was entirely awestruck, coming across another human this far away from home felt so eerie, someone who knew his name, a billion questions launched in his mind and he removed his helm.

"How do you even know it, my name?"

"I know everything Emin, about you, and what has led you here"

The astronaut gazed at the old man, he had an odd sense of familiarity to him, "Earth received coordinates to this place, they sent me here, and did you send them to earth?"

"I might as well say you sent them"

"That's impossible I just got here"

"Maybe, but you've always been here" the old man smiled at him.

"What is that supposed to mean?"

"Even if I tell you, you will not understand"

"Then make me understand, what's happening here, what is this place?" Emin insisted, the curiosity in him was getting far too intense.

"The place we stand in right now is remarkable, remarkable in the sense that right now we talk at the precise center of the universe, some things work quite differently here"

"What things?"

"Several things, time for instance is different in this place, entropy stops for any being inside this cavern, I've lived here for a millennia and yet you see me standing in front of you, while i was in here I didn't even age a second" the old man explained.

"A millennia? When did you even arrive here?" Emin asked.

"The same time as you just did right now, although in the previous universe" the old man looked him in the eye.

"That does not make any sense, what does the previous universe mean?"

"I can understand the reason behind your skepticism, first you need to change your perspective on time, and soon everything will make sense, tell me Emin, how do the scientists back home believe the universe to have started in the first place?"

"Well The big bang model tends to be the most widely accepted, it states how in the past that there was nothing, just a singularity and the big bang triggered a cosmic expansion giving rise to the universe as we know it into existence."

"Close enough, very close save for one huge aspect. They're mistaken, there wasn't a singularity before it, the universe did not start from absolutely nothing, it started from remains of a crunched down universe that existed prior to the one which exists right now".

"Oh yeah, and what existed before that universe" Emin questioned but he figured the answer himself. "Another universe of course and more before it"

"Precisely, an infinite loop in which a universe shrinks down to a tiny spot and explodes again in a big bang restarting everything"

"Wait, so if you were from a previous universe, why weren't you destroyed along with it?"

The old man gestured Emin to walk beside him, traversing the cavern, "it's like I said, things work differently here, the place we're in does exists outside normal space and time, the outside might get completely razed yet nothing would change in the inside, this isn't simple cave, look to the skies"

Emin lifted his head to gaze at the top at the luminescent glow and as he looked closely into the glow he realized it wasn't just a glow, he was looking at endless far away stars, nebulas, supernovas, there was no roof, just a seemingly endless universe as far as he could see.

"What's out there, is there anything more to it, or is it just a sparkling spectacle to be gazed upon by us" Emin said.

The old man laughed quietly at the question "that is an answer that you'd have to seek for yourself, for it is not my journey neither my life"

"What was your journey then, who are you?"

"Forgive me, I thought the answer was obvious enough for you to figure out on you own, don't you get it, I am you."

"Is that a metaphor for something I'm supposed to know?" the astronaut said but then he noticed the old man's clothes in the slight glow, they were faded and in rags almost yet were almost identical to the uniform issued to him, the one he was wearing under his space suit, he stopped short.

"There is no metaphor, my name is Emin and I am you from the previous iteration of the universe, you see all the universes have been an exact replica of the previous one, and nothing changed from the smallest incident to the largest occurrences, I came here exactly as you did, aboard the Sagan-V, in my time"

"Huh, nothing changed? How can that be, this would mean that we humans, we've no free will, if everything's happening as it had always happened, who knows how many times, what do any of our choices even amount to?"

"Your choices are your own, no one else is choosing for you, so we do have free will although since there is no way of knowing what happened in your previous iteration, you'd choose what you had always chosen"

"Oh I see, if I don't know what happened last time, it wouldn't matter what happens now even when the same occurred a number of times already, so we've all lived our lives a billion times over without knowing it?"

"You're right, although the universe does have its strange tricks, however subtle they maybe, are you familiar with déjà vu" the old man asked.

"I am, it's a feeling of familiarity in a new situation, as if it had happened before or one has already lived through it, psychologists attribute it to disassociation in memory, the simplest explanation"

"That might be so, but another justification for the phenomenon could be our consciousness retaining some odd memories throughout the loops, although it's nothing strong enough to influence our decisions, just a short and fleeting sentiment, quite irrelevant for our brains to actively process"

Emin stared at the masses of the cosmos he could see above him, a unique sight, but it didn't overwhelm him so much anymore, somehow he felt much relaxed now, and there was nothing to be startled about now. But he still had questions; "How did you even come to know anything about all of this?"

"You stay in this place long enough, everything starts to make sense after a while, or maybe the source of the knowledge isn't this place and instead my own mind, slowly releasing its tapped knowledge throughout these years of seclusion, being here."

At this remark Emin recalled reading about an ancient Greek philosophy, which stated that all kinds of knowledge was already present in the human brain and new discoveries were simply that knowledge being unraveled in a gradual way, perhaps if he'd stay he would get to learn everything as well.

"Why didn't you go back then, to share everything you learnt with the rest of the people back on earth?"

The old man halted in his steps for a brief moment, "You think I didn't want to? I asked the same exact question to myself millennia ago, all of this has happened before, I stood exactly where you're standing and asked myself the same question"

"And what was the answer?" the astronaut asked the old man only to be met by a sudden silence, "Look just tell me"

"The truth is that there was nothing to go back to, I was told by myself that earth was no more, had been destroyed in a nuclear attack frenzy between several nations, everything was finished, I was skeptical of course but accepted later that this was how things were now and I'm telling you the same now"

"Huh, you mean I can't go back, where am I supposed to go then?"

"Do not be disappointed so much, you've everywhere you can go now Emin, for this is the gateway to an endless universe, you can take your craft and explore the cosmos for everything there is, there are millions of worlds out there, all kinds of spectacles, the choice is yours to go and seek them all out for yourself, the only limit would be your human lifespan"

"Why would I rather not try and make my way back home on earth instead for the off chance that you've been wrong all along the way"

The old man shrugged, "Try it, make contact if you can with earth, the answer you receive will be silence or go back to find a barren earth and waste away the rest of your lifetime for the journey to earth and back here is too long for you and the craft you're here in"

Emin contemplated his options for a while now, there was no way Sagan-V would be enough to make a two way journey from here to earth and back again, at least if he chose to seek out his own journey he'd make it back to this place to prevent himself from dying, it did seem very enticing to him; immortality. "You came back didn't you? After seeing it all"

"Indeed I did, for who else would've been your messenger if I hadn't come back"

"One thing still does not make sense, the coordinates, who sent them?"

Hearing this query the old man reached into his rags and pulled out a device, one that was the same as the navigation device he had used to get here, "I did and so will you when the time comes, don't worry you'll know when to do it and its not anytime soon"

"This isn't strong enough to transport a signal back to earth from this far away"

"I assure you, if you send the same coordinates you've right now from this place they will reach the earth when it comes to existence again and when it is the right time for it"

The astronaut realized that he himself had been the one to send the coordinates, they didn't come from an alien intelligence, and he had been led here by coordinates from his own earlier self and was still coming to terms with the whole situation.

"Well what now, the craft doesn't have the capacity for two humans aboard, what happens to you?"

The old man motioned towards the far off shimmering entrance Emin had come in through "The moment I walk out of that doorway, I'm going to fade to nothingness, I do not belong here and have overdid my time in this universe and it's time for you to take your rightful place now, my voyage is over, let me walk you out"

The astronaut joined the old man in his walk towards the exit, it was time to part ways, with his own self it could be said, right now it was time for him to seek out his journey to an entire universe of endless possibilities that awaited him, he saw the passage and walked through it.

***

After a splash of whiteness Emin found himself back to the extraterrestrial planet, he looked behind hoping the old man would be right beside him although there was nothing between the passage and him but a bunch of timeworn spacesuit rags, the old man had faded from the world now.

Emin, regardless started on his stride back towards his spacecraft, he felt like the wisest man in the universe at this particular moment; something that might as well have been true, looking at the skies he'd be traversing across very shortly Emin felt exalted, of all the billions of human beings who had lived and died long before him and all the billions who he had shared the earth with he was the one who had come farther than any man had, as he always would and there was still much further to go, sighing with relief the astronaut finally saw the Sagan-V on the horizon like a loyal steed, eagerly awaiting him.

The Bar

Oliver sat on a barstool, one that was quite disproportionate to his physique. So with his hands lurched on the table and vision barely at par with that of the bartender's he called for a drink,

"The usual?" the bartender inquired as he gulped down a glass of water.

"Huh? It's my first time here" Oliver said.

"Well given that you're here at two in the afternoon it's obviously not your first time in a bar though".

"Fair enough, how about a glass of water as well". Oliver looked around; apparently he was the only one in aside from the bartender.

"Alright one serving of self-reflection coming right up" This made Oliver grin.

"What's your name mate?" Oliver said

"The name's Lazan"

"Oliver".

"Pleasure meeting you Oliver" the bartender said handing him a glass of water. Chugging the water Oliver rose from the barstool, ready to move on and head out.

"You know what, the bar is probably going to be empty until evening and it's frigid in here, want to get some sun outside for a minute"Lazan said.

"The sun, yeah that wouldn't be too bad I guess".

The two men headed outside, Sighting a bench by the curb Oliver sat down with the bartender following behind. The road in front of them separated by a strip of greenery was deserted like the Sunday afternoon that it was, with the occasional public transport bus driving by.

On the other side of the road was a street quite similar to theirs with an assortment of bars, restaurants, clothing stores and the like lined up almost symmetrical to the other side.

"What's all this for?" Oliver asked after a brief period of silence.

"Huh?"

"What's all this for, why're we here?" Oliver said.

"You mean in general or is that a rhetorical question?"

"Look around, what do you see?"

"Well the road, the shops, the sky, you know the works".

"How do we even know whether they're real?" Oliver said.

This made the bartender recoil, the conversation had become existential a bit too soon for his liking, it wasn't even evening yet.

"I don't know, maybe because we can see the sky, feel the breeze on our faces, and hear the distant rumbling of car engines in the distance".

"And that makes all of it real?"

"Look you need to tone down schopenhauer, i just wanted some sun alright".

"Some sun? Don't you realize, it's not real, this place doesn't even feel real, the sun isn't warm, the breeze isn't even cool, and it's all a lie"

"How are you so sure of that?" the bartender said.

"Alright let me ask you a question, what did you do today?"

"Ah well I was in the bar and you called for a drink, what does it matter?"

"So where were you before that?"

"I was uh, damn i was-".

"You don't remember do you? I figured that much" said Oliver

The bartender was quite taken aback, he felt uneasy as he continuously failed to recall where he was before entering the bar in the morning, in fact he couldn't recall any single aspect of his life other than entering the bar, reality started to feel dicey, even his name stopped making sense to him, it sounded made up.

"Oh fuck, who am I? Who are you, why're we here? "The bartender said.

"That's what I asked a minute ago".

"What the fuck is going on?"

"Look, I don't know, all i can say is something is off, something has always been off, and the last thing I can remember is sitting on a barstool and calling for a drink". Oliver said.

"That doesn't make sense, why would both of us not have any recollection of our lives other than a single moment in the bar?"

The situation was getting fretful as it progressed, none of this was regular.

"All I know is that when i said that it's my first time in the bar, I had a strong feeling that it wasn't true, it was as if my thoughts weren't even my own, I mean I asked for a glass of water in a bar, why would I do that?" Oliver said.

"It's almost as if-, as if our actions aren't our own" the bartender said. Even he didn't fully understand the clear meaning of that statement, his thoughts dwelled on the bar, he didn't know what it was called, who owned it, if anyone else worked there,it was all a clean slate.

"If they aren't our own, then who do they belong to?"

Oliver's mind was in a state of complete bewilderment, things didn't make sense anymore and he was no closer to the great yes than the bartender.

"You're the one who called all this out first, how did you realize this?"

"I don't really know mate, it just occurred to me that sitting out here was a bit out of the ordinary, I mean what kind of bartender just asks a bar patron to join him for some bloody sun outside?".

"Alright I'm going to ignore your sudden adoption of the British accent you're going with, let's approach the situation a bit of reason alright, what do we know? I know I am Lazan, I was in the bar and you called for a drink".

"I think we are not real".

"Huh, what was that?"

"Well, it seems like the only rational explanation doesn't it? We seem too abstract to be real".

"It's almost as if we're characters, fictional". The bartender said, the thought did make sense, the bar, and the lack of recollection of anything beside the simple moment in the bar, it was all too obvious to ignore.

"Yes characters, in some damn joke or a book". Oliver said in agreement.

The bartender looked back at Oliver, "Yes that would explain your weird British accent a moment ago, you're being retconned!"

"Preposterou-, I mean what the heck? What's a retcon?"

"It's a revision in a work of fiction that imposes a different interpretation on previously described events or characters" Lazan explained.

"Well I'll be damned Webster, you just had that definition on hand didn't you?"

"Actually I did" Lazan said as he held out his phone to reveal he had just googled the word retconned and read out the definition to him.

"Wow all of this is so absurd but looking at this situation from a third person perspective I'd say it's a pretty amusing one, if this was a story, I'd read it right to the end"

"The end yeah, I do wonder how this is going to end, or is this even going to end, what if we're meant to be stuck in this loop forever? The bar, this bench and that's it, that's all our lives" Lazan said startlingly.

"Does it occur to you we're written more like characters in a play rather that a story, it's all dialogue and no action, we're bloody theatre!" Oliver exclaimed.

"Wait a second, even if we were characters written in a play or a story or whatever at least we'd be self-aware, that's gotta make a difference".

Oliver suddenly stood up from the bench and looked around with a quick glance, "Once one realizes the true nature of human life he ascends into an observer of the theatre known as life rather than a mere actor, obediently playing his role".

"That is actually so profound, how did you even come up with that?"

"It's amazing, it just entered my mind and I said it out loud, quite dope huh?" Oliver replied as he sat back down.

Lazan adopted a much somber look now, "How come I don't get to say any profound stuff, I try to think but it's useless, all I can come up with is stupid light bulb jokes, am I meant to be just a simple snarky bartender? Is that all there is to me?"

Oliver patted Lazan's shoulder in a bid to uplift him, "That cannot be true, I believe the only thing you're meant to be is whatever you want to be"

"Oh god damn Oliver, That is another profound statement, can't you chill for a while and just talk about trees or cars or something" the two men burst into laughter, their conversation had finally taken a lighter tone.

"That was funny, I guess our dialogue was getting a bit blue, needed some comic relief"

"On that note I've a great light bulb joke; how many writers does it take to fix a light bulb?" Lazan asked as Oliver shrugged in confusion.

"Just one, though it's going to take like six months for him to get into his 'zone' and finally be able to do it" Lazan said.

Oliver laughed at this inane joke as it strangely made sense.

"A writer huh, I think whoever's writing us has run out of ideas for us, he's just making this up as he goes" Oliver said.

"I think it's worse than that, what if we're just fillers?"

"What's a filler?" Oliver said.

"You know those episodes in Television shows that are unrelated to the main plot and only serve to take up space, that's a filler" lazan explained.

"I see google again?"

"Of course" Lazan said as he gestured towards his phone's screen.

"So we're just supposed to take up space in a book, we don't have any relevance to the main plot whatsoever, sucks to be us I guess"

Lazan sat silently in contemplation for a while before he launched into a little monologue; "Well I'd agree to disagree my friend, sure a filler's primary function is to take up space, but I feel that there's more to fillers than just that, I believe that they are quite relevant in the sense that they add further to the theme of the plot, they provide an extra level of depth to the main plot which would be somewhat shallow without the cushion of a filler, think of it like cream in coffee, it is not the main ingredient but without it coffee wouldn't taste as wonderful as it usually does, there'd be something missing"

"I prefer Americano but I got your point mate, also look at you, now you're the one making profound statements!" Oliver said.

"Yes you're right, looks like I got retconned myself as well huh?"

Oliver nodded in agreement as he looked around their surroundings once again, the streets, the buildings as he had a stark observation. "Why do you think completed buildings are called buildings, they're already finished, shouldn't they be called a 'built'?"

As absurd as the joke was the two men nevertheless burst into spontaneous laughter.

"Look at that, more comic relief for us, I wonder if the rest of the book is a bit dark, maybe we're not fillers after all, we're the light side, our role is much bigger I'd say, we don't need to be nihilistic anymore" Lazan said as Oliver strongly agreed, they weren't pointless space taking fillers, they were the comic relief, bright glowing candles in the night.

The two men seemed much content in their roles, they didn't feel as existential as they had before, they had a purpose now and nothing other than that mattered, their purpose was everything.

"Our purpose is everything! All we need to do now is make sure we keep the jokes coming and we should be okay" Oliver said.

"Yes indeed, let's just sit here on this bench for nothing but an eternity and try to be somewhat funny" Lazan said.

"Sounds like a plan!"

Oliver and Lazan sat back in the bench waiting for an odd joke or a funny observation to pop into their mind but nothing popped, the men had gone blank, out of material.

"Whoa it's getting a bit scary now, my mind's running blank, Since we realized our purpose is to be funny I cannot think of anything, it's like my mind got a factory reset" Oliver said.

"I know right, same with me, I don't think we were meant to realize our purpose, perhaps we're cursed to constantly seek purpose, maybe that's what our role here is, we're supposed to pursue meaning for as long as we exist until we don't" Lazan remarked.

Oliver glanced around the lonesome street, the sun was fading into the horizon and it was almost time for dusk.

"It's getting dark" Oliver remarked.

"Of course it is, we're purpose seeking beings in a purposeless universe"

"No, I meant like for real, take a look around will you?"

Sure enough, the sun had set giving way to the darkness and the night covered the street now, with car engines rumbling in the distance and a half-moon in the sky, there was an even piercing silence in their environs.

The silence was abruptly interrupted by a sudden beeping noise which startled the men.

"The hell's that noise, am I finally going crazy or do you hear it too?" Oliver asked.

"I hear it too, where is it coming from" Lazan looked to their surrounding hoping to find an answer but to no effect, the beeping voice continued, puzzling the men.

"Wait, it's coming from your pocket, your phone's ringing" Oliver said as he pointed at the bartender's front pocket, sure enough the beeping noise was Lazan's phone ringing constantly, he took it out and picked up the call.

Oliver zoned out, looking at people who had now come out onto the streets while the bartender attended the phone call. He wondered how those people saw themselves, did they think of themselves as being just like the other guy walking in front of them on the street, *Nah, pretty sure each one of them had a narrative going on in their heads that made them think they were not like the others; a common human affliction,* Oliver thought as he turned to the bartender, now done with the call facing him.

"So who was on the phone?" Oliver inquired.

The bartender was silent, sitting frozen on the bench looking rather dazed. It took a good while for him to give an answer.

"That was- that was the bar owner, and this is weird but he was asking where I have been the whole day, apparently the bar had patrons coming in all this while and finding it without a bartender, who is me, I'm the bartender!"

"Yes you're the bartender, what's so shocking about that?"

The bartender's face suddenly lightened up, "That's not just it; I know who I am now! It all came back to me during the call, I'm Lazan, I've a family, I've a home, I know where I grew up and everything, don't you see it? I'm not a damn concept anymore; I'm a person, a real person!" He said zealously.

Before a surprised Oliver could say anything he was interrupted by a single sharp ringing sound coming from his phone as well, he took the phone out of his pocket and discovered that he had received a message; a text from his wife!

As he read the simple text from his wife asking him when he'd be getting back home everything started coming back to Oliver as well; He was married with children, he had a job as a data analyst, a home, a decent sedan and he was getting late for dinner.

"Well I'll be damned my friend, it appears that I happen to be a person too and I should be getting back home now" Oliver said as he rose up from the bench.

Lazan, likewise got up from the bench; "And I should get back to the bar now, there's some patrons in as I'm told"

There was a strange moment of silence shared by the two men as the street went on around them.

"I guess this is farewell then comrade, goodbye"

"Goodbye brother"

The men shook hands and took off in different directions and to their separate destinations and lives, with the bartender heading back to the bar for now and Oliver going back home to his wife.

They walked ordinarily in a calm manner, completely indistinguishable from anyone else walking on the street in that moment, yet they walked with their minds still perplexed over the day's strange events and the conversations they had shared together.

The whole day had been rather absurd, unanimously they both decided to not dwell on it too much and keep on going about with their lives as they had always done.

The Prison

The prisoner awoke in a brightly lit white cell wearing a grey jumpsuit, having no memory of how he got there or who he was he glanced at his surroundings, another man sat on the opposite bed wearing a similar grey jumpsuit looking at him, becoming more awake by every second the prisoner opened his eyes fully and sat up in his bed.

"You're finally awake; I was getting a bit worried over here, what's your name?"

"My name, I'm sorry but I don't really remember?" he uttered as he realized he didn't even know what his name was or where he came from, he was a blank canvas.

"Oh, that's alright, I don't remember mine either, I'm talking about the title on your wrist tag, what's it say?"

The prisoner saw a black device strapped on his left hand, he lifted his wrist up to his face to get a closer look. It had his supposed name written in electronic text on the screen; *Mikael.*

"It says Mikael, though I'm not sure I've heard that name ever before"

"You bet, mine says Hazlitt, I didn't even know that was a name, but these are our names now"

"Wait, how long have you been here?" Mikael was puzzled how the other guy seemed to already know more than him.

"I woke up a good ten minutes before you, gave me enough time to feel the strap around my wrist and check out my name"

"What else do you know about this place, why're you in here" Mikael wanted to find out as much as he could about the place he'd ended up in.

"It seems like some sort of prison that's obvious, I have no idea what I'm here for or who I was before waking up here"

"Well, join the club mate, I've no clue either"

Their conversation was broken by the sound of several footsteps passing through beyond their cell door; the door was entirely white similar to the rest of the cell, Mikael surprisingly noticed a handle on their side of the door. "Huh, that's odd"

"What's odd?

"The door, why's there a handle on our side, shouldn't that be on the other side for the guards?" Mikael got up and moved towards the door as Hazlitt looked on eagerly, he wrapped his hand around the handle and gave it a slight pull downwards, the door swayed open.

"Now that's interesting, we're not locked" Hazlitt got up and joined Mikael by the door side. They peeked through the gap and saw several men walking through the corridor.

"You think we should go out and take a walk?"

"Thought you'd never ask" Hazlitt swung open the door and walked right out, Mikael followed.

The two of them started walking among the rest of the prisoners through the corridor, they saw a few prison guards standing by, covered from head to toe in black riot gear with faces hidden by baklavas and helmets with a tinted visor, the corridor opened and led them into a common area of sorts, it looked like a huge brightly lit hall full of prisoners and connected by many corridors from all sides leading to it, they deduced it must be the central location of the prison.

It was full of the hustle-bustle of prisoners sitting in groups, standing by and conversing. Mikael noticed that there were two kinds of prisoners in there; some of them were wearing grey jumpsuits like theirs and the others were in blue jumpsuits, although he noticed that the greys and blues weren't mixed together and everyone was surrounded by their own respective color group without intermingling.

"Who do you think these other guys in blue are, why are they in a different color?" Hazlitt had been observing the same thing.

"Allow me to answer that, boys" a prisoner came up behind them and patted their shoulders making them turn around to face him, he had the same grey jumpsuit as them.

"And who the heck are you?" Mikael asked, he wasn't going to allow himself to be intimidated my anyone in here.

"Uh apologies for the abrupt approach, I'm a fellow grey, the name's Mitch as the wrist tag says right here, you two look new around here"

"Arrived twenty minutes ago so yeah, we're new" Hazlitt scanned the man to get a measure of him, Mitch did look like someone whose been here a while he judged, he could be helpful.

"Let's sit down for a little orientation then, shall we?" Mitch gestured towards a recently emptied table and they followed him to it and the three of them sat down on the attached benched.

After some brief introductions about their names and not remembering anything else about themselves; Mikael and Hazlitt saw fit to seek answers to the many questions puzzling them.

"So you didn't tell us yet, who are the men in blue?"

"Well I don't really talk to them much, none of the greys do to be honest, they are their own people and don't want much to do with us either" he explained

"What's the difference then, between the greys and blues?"

"No one knows for sure, but word goes around that they're the worse lot of criminals than us, violent offenders most likely, we the greys are probably here for minor crimes I'm sure, Hazlitt over here probably didn't file his taxes at the right time" the three men started laughing in unison, yet Mikael was still curious about the blues.

"But no one knows right? Nobody knows for sure what they're in for?" Mikael said

"That's right, but just look at the greys around man, they're our kind and we belong with them, who knows what kind of sociopaths the blues are, there's not much communication between our type and theirs"

"So each color stays with his own, can't I go around and sit down with them like we're sitting right now?" Hazlitt's curiosity had been provoked as well.

"That's right, sure you want to go and blend in with those people, be my guest, but I don't want anything to do with those criminals, we're civilized people after all, let's not compromise that"

"How do we even know for sure were not the worse criminals, what if it's just a random uniform without any meaning?" Mikael was skeptical about the whole concept, unwilling to believe that color dictated who they were.

"That's not a very popular opinion here brother, don't go around saying that too much is what I'd suggest, well it cannot be random, the different colors have to mean something, I don't believe otherwise" Mitch was very defensive of the notion.

The men sat in silence for a while contemplating the nature of the place and there was still so much more to know. However curiosity kept grasping them and they wanted to know everything there was to know about the prison and how it worked, where it was and Mitch slowly explained as much as he could;

All of the prisoners in there had woken up similarly to them without a memory of their crime or their lives, something that they never get to find out apparently and as time went by they all accepted their fate and the prison become their life.

Their new names were their new identities, no one ever got out of the prison and the prisoners lived and died in the prison itself, their bodies disposed quickly unseen by the others and not much memory of their existence left behind, they just went away.

"So who runs this place, whose holding us here?" Mikael said, the more he knew, the less everything made sense.

"No one runs this place, its hella crazy I know, but there is no authority that rules over the prison" Mitch explained.

"And what about the guards and the staff?", Hazlitt enquired. The prison didn't seem like a place of anarchy to him, it seemed quite organized.

"You see the guards are prisoners too, so is the other prison staff and so is the warden himself, the prisoners run this place themselves, there is no outside intervention"

Mitch went on to explain how everyone in the prison had a job to do, one could work in the food industry or in maintenance services, or they could apply to become a prison guard, which if selected for they'd then go through rigorous training in the dedicated prison training academy and pass out as a prison guard along with the perks included. All the guards and all the staff were prisoners too; such was the system inside the prison.

The men had been sitting for quite a while now and decided to get up and talk as they walked around the prison, they got up and proceeded to move towards the indoor yard, everything in the prison was indoors, there was no outside for the prisoners. Mikael and Hazlitt urged Mitch to explain the system further.

Mitch described how even the warden was a prisoner himself, a grey like them, elections were held every 6 years for the position of the prison warden and several administrative posts, the elections were approaching nearer and were presided over by a prisoner comprised election commission, apparently the prisoners ruled themselves.

Mikael was quite taken aback, he didn't expect the prison to be a democratic institution, and it seemed very peculiar. "Tell me more about this warden"

"Oh he's a man by the name of Russel, quite a cherished leader, he's one of us after all, before this all the previous wardens have been blues, and it was about time we had a grey warden, our own people leading us." Mitch said, he seemed to be quite the fan of this Russel.

"So any of us could become warden, even me and you?" Hazlitt said

"Ideally we can, it's a bit difficult in reality though, the prison directives do state that anyone here could become warden given they secure a comfortable majority but that part is a bit tricky"

"Oh, how so?" Mikael asked

"You see, it's hard for people here to have a common idea of who they want to be the warden, like I said the greys don't support the blues and vice-versa, and even the groups are divided among themselves so the only way for someone to be a significant candidate is to join a party or a focus group within either of the two groups and that's next to impossible for people like us"

"People like us, what's that supposed to mean?"

"Oh you know, average guys, without much capital loaded into our wrist tags, no one cares about our beliefs if we're broke, we're irrelevant to everyone, the parties wouldn't let us in if we can't afford the buy in, that's how they retain their exclusivity"

Mikael contemplated silently as they entered the huge indoor yard, he observed the surroundings; the ceiling was high as the eye could see and well lit, almost looked like sunlight, sunlight that wasn't warm. The walls were white and everything looked superficially advanced.

"I see, we carry our earned money in these tags, how would I make like a lot of it?" Hazlitt asked as he broke the silence.

"You won't, most likely you'll keep working the same job you first get and all your money would be spent on your prison expenses, your meals, passes into different sections, buying utilities, stuff like that, I'd advise you both to start looking for a job as soon as possible or you'd fall down in your social status"

"Our status, what's that now?" Hazlitt said as the three men now stopped to avoid a group of blues passing through and then carried on.

"Everyone here has a social status, it depends on your average money and what kind of job you have, the higher your position is the more people respect you and you get certain privileges like access to this very yard and further eligibility to apply for other jobs, now everyone who arrives here comes with some amount of credit to their name, consider it a grace period, but the credit gets deducted as you move through or use the prison facilities like standing here just now or going to the mess, basically everything though"

"So I've to pay for myself being in prison, why don't I simply kill myself?"

"You wouldn't be surprised that most people actually do" Mitch glanced at Hazlitt in the eyes.

"I see, well what happens if I use up all my credit and don't earn more, couldn't I still live here, without spending anything?"

"You'd live but not here, for the guards will transfer you section 9 if you don't have any credit left, and you don't want to live there, the living conditions are just horrible, everyone's cramped up, there aren't any facilities, it's chaos there, we call it 'the slum', once you get demoted down there there's not much chance of moving back up in your social class again"

Mikael had learnt enough about the prison for the day; it was too much to comprehend at once and he wanted to take a walk and see more of the prison by himself, he took his leave from the other men and strolled away towards one of the exit corridors.

"Just stay away from the blues and be careful around, you seem like a decent guy, I hope i see you in the morning then" Mitch remarked.

Mikael nodded in agreement and gradually walked away along the brightly lit corridors with the aim of exploring the prison, with a million questions still on his mind, he saw groups of greys and groups of blues walking separately, prisoners using their wrist-tags to purchase access to different areas inside the prison, the prison had it all, cafeterias, gyms, even a bar and an entire shopping center, although everything had a fee and not everyone could afford it.

He found the whole system rather strange; even though all the inhabitants were prisoners themselves and there was no outside interference the prison still remained such a divided place when it could've been just easily a utopia for all of the prisoners inside instead of a select few who could afford everything.

Looking at his wrist tag, he wondered if the credit loaded even had any kind of value it, just a bunch of digital numbers was all that they were after all.

I need to get out of here, this place isn't for me. Mikael thought as he saw the never-ending metallic corridors and hallways winding throughout the place, it was at this moment he began plotting his escape; every prison can be broken out of after all.

As Mikael walked through a common hall he saw a couple of guards walking towards him with a steady pace, he stopped right there in his tracks, fearful of what comes next and turned around to see a group of blues standing a few meters back.

The two guards walked up to him and one of them grabbed Mikael violently by the collar, "hey grey, don't you know this is a blue common hall, get the hell out of here" the first guard said.

"So what, can't I walk through?" Mikael protested.

Hearing this, the other guard hit him over the shoulder with his baton; Mikael pushed the guard back defensively. At this action of his the guard hit him on across the face with his baton while the other held guard held him down, Mikael saw red over his eyes and dropped to the cold white floor.

With a blurred vision, Mikael saw the group of blues he'd seen earlier running towards the guards standing over him. The blues asked the guards to back off the new prisoner; the guards retreated hastily after threatening severe retaliation for defying them.

Mikael awoke to find the blues standing around him, two of them helped him get back up his feet, Mikael seemed disarrayed as he saw the blues helping him get up and asking if he was okay, from what he'd learnt so far the blues weren't supposed to aid him in anything and right now they had just fought off against the guards for him.

"Why'd you help me, I'm a grey, not one of your own" Mikael said.

One of the blues walked up to him, "Just cause you don't wear the same colors as us doesn't mean we're enemies, now the guards are going to come back here with large numbers any time, It's best if you find your way back to your cell as quickly as you can" he said as he patted Mikael on the shoulder. The blues began to disperse and Mikael hurried his way out as well and on to his cell.

The days went by quickly after that incident, Mikael would wake up in his cell with Hazlitt, do the jobs assigned to him later in the day, like the rest of the prisoners, and then he'd eventually sit down for lunch with Hazlitt and Mitch, who had quite promptly taught them all he knew about the prison. After lunch it'd be back to work for the boys and so on. Such was life and the days turned into weeks which turned into month.

On one such lunch though that broke the monotony of everyday life in the prison Mikael sat down with the two men and said; "I want to get out, I'm done with this place; the meaningless jobs, the unnecessary conflicts and rivalries, the complete absurdity, I want out of it all". Mitch and Hazlitt stared back at him.

"Who doesn't, I'm coming with you" Mitch said with Hazlitt smiling in agreement.

"No, I'm being serious right now, there must be some way out of this place, we just need to know where, there must be more to life than this place" Mikael retorted.

"Even if there was a way out, none of the common prisoners seem to have any idea about it" Hazlitt added in.

Mitch seemed to have a thought right then; "Right, none of the common prisoners, but what about the not so common prisoners, perhaps the warden knows something we don't, perks of the post, we just need to figure out a way to sneak into the warden's office"

Mikael looked at Mitch and nodded in agreement, they had a lot to plan.

***

The days passed by while Mitch tried to figure out a way to sneak into the warden's office, the warden in the prison had become a largely unseen figure by now, rarely seen by any of the prisoners save for a couple of prison guards who'd occasionally go in and out of his office on the furthest corner of the prison at an unspecified location. Mitch would track the guards supposed to be in charge of the warden and follow them in the hope of finding a short route to get in the warden's office but all his efforts were in vain as he'd always track the guards to a gated off corridor from where he couldn't follow the guards anymore as the gate shut down after the guards' entry.

Mikael's desire to find a way out of the prison and discover what was out there had been quite contagious for Mitch as he dedicated himself to helping the boys, after so many meaningless and drudging years at the nameless prison; he'd finally got a purpose. Mitch noticed that on every third day there were only two guards going through the corridor gate instead of the usual four guards, he realized that there was a way to get into the warden's office but it would come at a cost.

The following day, Mikael and Hazlitt walked into the sleek cafeteria bustling with prisoners going about the same lives they had always gone through, Mikael was excited with the prospect of making a different way, the men saw Mitch sitting at a table alone waiting for them, apparently with some information, Mikael hoped.

Mitch updated the men on the information he'd discovered, about the guards going through a corridor gate and on to the warden's office and told them about the lesser number of guards on every third day, this would give them an advantage should it come to fight. The three men decided to initiate their plan two days from now.

The next two days arrived rather quickly, the three men met right before lunch hours, when most of the prisoners and guards would be confined to the cafeterias. At that moment they felt restless, thrilled at the prospect of what lay ahead.

"So this is really happening huh?" Hazlitt said, his voice trembling to the point of almost breaking off. He felt cold even in the temperature controlled lobby.

"Yes we are, let's get this over with" said Mitch as Mikael just nodded in agreement and they turned into one of the many sleek corridors of the prison and started walking hurriedly with Mitch leading them. A million thoughts raced inside Mikael's head, *how were they even going to pull this off?* He wondered.

They tracked the two guards going towards the warden's office and tailed them from a distance until they got to the corridor gate; it was time for everything to go down now.

Mitch sprinted to the guards and jumped them as soon as the gate was unlocked and yelled for the two men to cross over to the other side, Mikael and Hazlitt reluctantly ran and crossed the gate despite their first instinct of going to the rescue of their friend while the guards struggled to move past Mitch who kept shoving them and blocking their way allowing his comrades to proceed to the warden's quarters.

As the yells of the guards faded in the distance the two men ran in unison towards the warden's office leaving behind Mitch to fend against the guards, It was time for all to be revealed, each sound made by their shoes against the cold floor got them closer to an answer of what the prison was and why they were here, Soon they'd find the truth and everything would be alright then.

They stopped right in their tracks as they found themselves facing the warden's office at the end of their way, Mikael kicked the door open and the two men went in. The warden jumped up from his chair as soon as he saw the men.

"Russel" Mikael said.

"So you boys finally made it here, to be fair I wasn't expecting you to reach all this way, looks like your friend outside really believe in you two" the warden calmly said.

"Stop with the games Russel, we're not here to play we're here for answers and you're going tell us everything" Hazlitt moved closer to the warden.

"What is it you think I can tell you?"

"All that you know about this prison, why are we here, more importantly how do we get out?" Mikael stepped forward, joining Hazlitt.

The warden burst into a cynical laugh confusing the two men.

"Huh? And what make you two think that I've any answer about all of that".

"You're the warden, you run this prison, stop trying to trick us or you're never getting out of this room" Mikael became more desperate, he hadn't come all this way for nothing.

"Sure I'm the warden and I run this place, for now at least but I'm afraid to admit that even I'm no closer than you when it comes to the answers that you seek, I was and I am a prisoner here too, just like you, I can understand your worry, you came all this way hoping to get some answers and now you look at me and realize that I'm no closer to the great yes than you are so I'm sorry to say your optimism is misplaced, I cannot give you the answers that you need".

"You are the warden, you must know something we don't, if this is a ploy to buy time it won't work, our friend outside will hold the guards back as long as it takes, It's in your best interest to tell us all you know" Hazlitt said with a sharp tone, Mikael on the other hand was frozen, coming to terms with what the warden was telling them.

"Your friend here is realizing I'm being nothing but honest, even as the warden I have no idea about what the prison is, why we are all here, I do not know of any ways out, all I know is how to run the prison which is surprisingly fairly easy, given how the prison practically runs itself, I don't really do much, my role is more of a ceremonial one you could say, giving the prisoners here the warm illusion of authority" The warden sat back again in his chair.

Hazlitt looked at a distraught Mikael who stood frozen, no more words left in him.

But Mikael was deep in thought, weighing their options, he did realize the warden was being honest about being entirely unaware about the prison, now they had no hope of finding out what the prison was and why they were here, the thing that vexed him was they had come this far and it was all going to be for nothing, their entire plan, going up in smoke, their journey had been pointless.

In the brief silence shared by the three men in the warden's office Mikael's eyes lit up as he had a sudden idea; sure they might never know what the prison was, they could never get out, but since they had come so far as to hold the warden hostage they could do one thing, they could change some things around here. Mikael knew the one thing they needed to make the warden do, He gestured the warden to listen to him.

"Alright Russel, we're done here, I'm will ask you to do one thing that's going to stop me from killing you right here and now since I've already come this far, you're going to go on the prison command interface and order the guards to let Mitch go to his cell unharmed and then you're going to make a simple announcement, from this moment forth you're doing away with the two uniform system, the guards are to collect all the uniforms from the prisoners, both blue and grey right away"

The warden's eyes shot up, "Are you insane, what do you hope to achieve by doing that?"

"It's simple Russel, the collected uniforms are all to be dyed black, the same color for all the prisoners and the guards and distributed back, no more different uniforms, we're all in the same boat, there's no point in wearing different colors, you do this and we'll peacefully walk out of here and you'll continue being the warden until your rightful term, are we in agreement?" Mikael said with a stern tone.

The warden looked him in the eyes and nodded slowly, he had no option but to agree.

As the warden reached the prison command interface to make their announcement Hazlitt looked at Mikael and smiled, acknowledging his genius, the simple act of changing the uniforms was going to have a snowball effect of making enormous changes in the prison.

***

The voice of the warden making this hasty and absurd announcement all over the prison faded in the distance as the two men walked back elatedly from the warden's office to rejoin their friend waiting back at his cell, the guards stood back silently and made way for them as they continued through the corridors.

They reached Mitch's cell and were greeted outside by a bunch of prisoners looking at them with a newfound reverence, Mitch walked out and joined them eagerly, realizing that their risky excursion hadn't been for nothing after all. As they saw prisoners starting to do away with their dual uniforms and handing them to the guards, the three men headed together towards the prison mess, a decent meal was long due.

The Detective
(A noir story)

The rain picked up and it started pouring heavier than before, the detective took shelter to the side of a hotel entrance, the noises down the street were overtaken by the sound of rain drops crashing down on the pavement.

The detective smiled cynically as he realized he had almost reached his destination. The purpose for the detective's visit to this particular hotel complex was retribution or rather justice as he liked to believe. In the earlier days all he wanted was power enough to change the world, all he had now was a revolver; his own personal instrument of justice.

Justice was what had brought the detective to this location, justice for a murdered senior associate; someone he used to look up to, almost like an elder brother. The detective's associate; a Mark Sidero had been found inexplicably dead a week ago without a single mark of injury on his body at his home leaving behind no clues except for one; the associate's wife had been missing since his death.

The wife had disappeared without a trace into the night, leaving behind a dead husband who had none to grieve after him or remember him, save for the eccentric detective who had been working with the man for half a decade. The detective was dead sure the wife was partially or completely involved in his murder, having fled supposedly after killing her spouse leaving no trail behind, until now.

With the autopsy report still due a major breakthrough had come to the detective when he found that his former partner's debit card had been used to check in at a particular hotel, it had led him to the hotel like a beacon in a dark forest. He knew the elusive wife was somewhere hidden amongst the corridors of this vast and decrepit hotel.

He looked around at the odd figures inhabiting the city corners; petty thieves, drug addicts, muggers and alike scum of society, all living in the dark places hidden throughout everyday civilization lurking in the shades, like an infestation refusing to go away.

The detective held the belief that the vast presence of criminals and scum was in fact a symptom, of a larger disease which has been plaguing human society in today's world; weakness, the reason everything had been seemingly going backwards for humanity was the prevalence of a culture of weakness with weak men who had frail minds, who couldn't bear the responsibility of their lives and turned into degenerates, addicts, criminals just for the lack of a better thing to do with their life. This was the cause behind the rapid decaying of society the detective felt was taking place in the world right now.

He let go of these intrusive thoughts and choose to dwell on a memorable day with his former associate instead;

It was calm Sunday afternoon; the two detectives had received a hefty paycheck for a recently closed case. Moods were quite elated and normally the detectives decided to celebrate by paying a visit to a bar in town the frequented from time to time.

The men walked into the wooden floor of the bar and called for the bartender only to find the bar empty and the bartender missing. The detective looked around but there wasn't a single soul in the bar.

"Well I'll be damned, looks like we've the establishment to ourselves pal" Mark had exclaimed.

The men laughed and instead of turning back and going home they decided to stay a while and serve themselves, and when all was done they left the bar quietly even leaving behind a generous tip for the bartender, regards of the detective's associate.

The detective reminisced of this peculiar incident and his associate with a brief smile that was cut short by a comprehension of the present reality. The associate was gone now; He had lost a good friend.

There was no bringing him back; all he could do was bring justice to a dead man. The detective speculated whether he should alert the cops first or go right in himself, *if I don't make my own choices, they will be made for me.*

He tucked his revolver under his coat to keep it hidden as he walked right in the hotel entrance. Inside the enormous structure of lilac walls he saw a single receptionist siting on the counter with her eyes glued to a computer screen.

He walked towards the reception. Soon he'd find the answers he was looking for and everything would be alright.

"Hello there"

The receptionist smiled looking up and asked how she could help him.

"I'm looking for an old friend who checked in here recently, someone by the name of Catelin Sidero, Do you mind pointing me to their room number"

"Sure, let me just go through the logbook and I'll let you know"

The detective waited as the receptionist frantically searched through the records, she seemed to be having no success at the task.

"Is there some kind of a problem?" He said gently.

"No, actually I just can't find anybody by that name to have checked into our hotel, I've gone through all the weekly and monthly records, there is no record of a Catelin Sidero checking in here"

"Are you sure?" The detective said with a firm tone.

"Yes absolutely, no one by that name has checked in here"

"Well that's quite odd, now I'm gonna need you to do me a small favor" He reached into his coat and rummaged with his fingers for a while as the receptionist apprehensively looked on.

The detective took out a crumpled sheet of paper; a Xerox of the debit card unfolded it and handed it to the receptionist.

"Now see, I know for sure that this card of hers was used recently to check in here and I need you to tell me who used this card here"

The receptionist looked at the card details and fixated back on her computer screen to find out which room was checked in with that particular card.

"Okay I think I got it, whoever used this card checked into room number 301, strangely I can't find any ID attached to the record"

"Not to worry, that's all I needed to know" He said as he turned towards the elevator and started walking.

"Wait, do I need to call the police?" The receptionist asked after him.

"Won't be necessary" The detective said without turning back.

A million questions blew up in his mind as he got in the elevator and pressed on the up button; How long was the wife planning on hiding out here, why wasn't there any record of her checking in there and so forth. Clueless, the detective stood calmly as the elevator went up

The elevator doors slid open on the third floor; his destination and the detective stepped out, not stopping until he reached room number 301.

When he got to the room the door was locked from inside, the detective knocked. After a brief moment of inaction the door swung open to reveal the sole occupant of the hotel room.

Instead of the missing wife he was hoping to find the detective saw a lanky man with a pale face looking at him anxiously. The pale faced man glanced at the door, thinking of making a run for it. A quick flash of the detective's revolver made that thought obsolete.

The detective gestured the pale faced man to get back in the room.

"Now I'm going to make this easy for you, I will ask you some questions, give me the answers and you can stay alive, simple as that" He pointed towards two chairs on the edge of the room and instructed the pale faced man to sit.

The man sat down flowed by the detective sitting on the chair facing him with a small hotel table in between.

"Alright, where is she pal?" The detective asked.

"Where's who man, I have no idea what you're talking about"

"Do you really want to make this difficult for you? I know for sure you checked in here on behalf of a certain woman by the name of Catelin Sidero and I will shoot you in the knee right now if you dare to deny that" The detective pulled out his revolver and placed it on the table.

The pale faced man's eyes shot up suddenly.

"Wait, Sidero, as in detective Mark Sidero? I work for him every now and then as a freelancer, do the occasional task that'd be too risky for him, he contacted me recently, wanted me to go on an assignment for him, gave me his debit card and asked me to check in here after a couple of days. He shrugged off my questions about the motive, said it was a high priority case and the less I knew, the better."

The detective was intrigued and shocked by the answer, "And how long ago did he actually contact you?"

"More than a week ago, I think it's been nine days, I checked in here five days after like he instructed me to do, I haven't heard from him since and he hasn't been answering his phone. Probably cause of the nature of the case, can you tell me how to contact him, I've grown restless staying here without anything to do"

"I don't think anybody can tell you how to contact him now, detective Mark Sidero is dead, he was found collapsed in his home a week ago"

The man jumped back in his chair, shocked at the piece of information he'd just received. Although his shock was nothing compared to the detective's dilemma, he was processing all the bits of facts he had just discovered. The detective raced his mind thinking of a motive for his associate to send a random man to check in at a hotel in the middle of the city with his debit card.

There has to be a good reason for it all, Mark was a smart man, not a person who'd do something for the hell of it.

Suddenly the detective's mind had an eureka moment; *of course, the only logical reason for Mark to send this man here anonymously with his debit card was using the man as a red herring, Mark wanted people thinking his wife had took off taking his debit card with him. The pale faced man being here at the hotel was a false clue, a distraction.*

But why would a dead man want people thinking his wife had run away? The answer was obvious; because he hadn't planned to die, his death was the deviation. The wife wasn't missing, she didn't run away. The associate's wife had been murdered by the associate himself was the likely conclusion; otherwise why go through all the effort trying to make people think his wife had run away. It was the perfect crime, until it wasn't.

The detective, still determined to find the wife picked up his revolver tucking it back into his coat. He took the hotel room key and without saying a word to the pale faced man he headed towards the door locking it from outside; *the pale faced man might be a useful witness later.*

He paced towards the elevator, intending to get to his car parked on a nearby street as soon as he could; he needed to go to Mark's house and look for any possible evidence he might have missed earlier.

***

The detective pulled up to his former associate's driveway in his beat down black sedan. He parked the car right next to the front door and got out as he set his sight on the white painted door of the house.

He rammed the door open and walked inside the main lobby, hoping to find a shred of new evidence.

Everything was so confusing now, just like life; *you keep walking through a path without questioning where you're going until suddenly the path ends and you're left hanging in the middle of uncertainty and chaos.*

Still determined to push through and solve the case the detective went towards the coach where Mark had been found dead. Everything was pretty much normal, nothing unusual that could catch the eye.

There was a transparent coffee table next to the couch; it held a single glass and a bottle of bourbon along with a tiny vase of now dead flowers.

Seeing the bottle laying on the table the detective remembered something he'd heard once, an adage; *if you really want to know a man, take a look at his medicine cabinet.*

He rushed towards the main washroom expecting to find something useful; he swung open the medicine cabinet behind a bathroom mirror and looked at the contents inside. There were a couple of codeine based cough medications, painkillers, benzos and all other usual stuff one would expect to find in the cabinet of someone in the crime industry.

Just as he was about to close the cabinet the detective's eye caught a medication container that had been left open, which was odd since all the other containers were sealed properly. He picked up the sole container and glanced at the label.

The open container had clozapine in it; an anti-psychotic medication which was used for extreme cases of mental disorders such as the likes of schizophrenia. Clozapine also happened to be a strong risk factor for causing an acute stroke when large doses were taken.

All the pieces suddenly fit together and the detective realized he had finally found the one bit of evidence that he was seeking all along; the detective's former associate had been the killer all along; Mark had murdered his wife for reasons unknown and later inadvertently caused his own death at the hands of his medication.

The answers that he had gotten only served to lead to more qualms. He remembered simpler times when the definition of good and bad had been clear. The detective couldn't accept that his long known associate and friend had been a murderer but the evidence was now clear.

The detective however, realized that he was punching above his weight now, he had done all that he needed to do and it didn't need to be his fight anymore. He pulled out his cellphone and placed a call to the police department letting them know all that he'd found.

***

The cops were on their way now and the detective walked out into the backyard, he pulled out a pack of cigarettes from his coat and lit one.

As he took the first drag of his cigarette the detective noticed a substantial patch of grass that was thinner than the rest of the grass in the lawn. He had no doubts as to what he'd find buried under there if he grabbed a shovel right now and started digging.

Regardless he made the decision to wait for the cops to arrive and continued smoking his cigarette standing in the middle of the lawn and gazing at the dusky sky.

As the life of the cigarette came to an end the detective finally came to terms with the events of the past week. He had cut through all the chaos to decipher the entire fiasco; collected all the evidence that needed to be collected, he even had a witness locked in a room at a particular hotel. There was a certain peace in the knowledge that the case had been solved and at the end of the day this was a win for him. The detective let off a slight smile as he heard the police sirens in the distance.

Acknowledgements

This book would not have been what it is if not for several wonderful people who contributed towards its publication one way or the other.

Firstly I want to thank the entire team, especially Brijesh Rai and Akshit Bagai for being so patient and accommodating during and before the publishing process. Thanks to Shivangi Lohia as well for the amazing cover.

I am grateful to the entire Team at White Falcon Publishing for making the Book project for 'The Existential Club' highly efficient and smooth.

I would also like to thank Linda Parrish of Druyan-Sagan associates for her timely coordination and clarifications regarding copyright permissions.

Huge thanks to John L. Seagull all the way from Germany for letting me use his work 'Persistence' in The Existential Club, I feel it really fits the tone of the book.

And lastly I want to thank all the people who continue to inspire me to follow my dreams and become the person I want to be.

- Shayaan Rehman

Lightning Source UK Ltd.
Milton Keynes UK
UKHW042205150223
417096UK00010B/207